MI NURSES
Association

P9-CMN-766

1

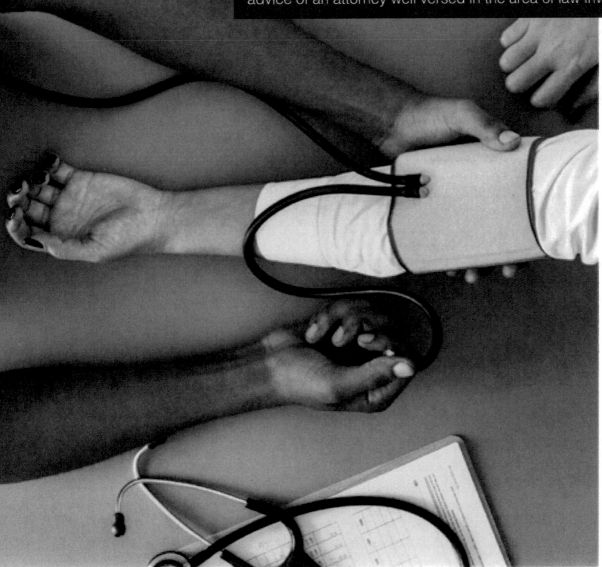

PROFESSIONAL & LEGAL REGULATION OF NURSING PRACTICE IN MICHIGAN

5TH EDITION

Professional & Legal Regulations of Nursing Practice in Michigan is intended to be a useful reference for all nurses, healthcare workers and individuals with an interest in the regulation of the nursing profession in Michigan. Laws and regulations, as well as how they are interpreted, are subject to change. Please be advised that interpretations or opinions contained in this publication may not be shared by regulatory agencies or the courts, and that the contents are not intended to be a substitute for competent legal advice. Nurses faced with a specific legal issue should seek the advice of an attorney well versed in the area of law involved.

ABOUT US

The Michigan Nurses Association (MNA) has been a professional association for nurses in Michigan for over 115 years. The vision of MNA is to be the association of choice to which every nurse belongs and benefits from education, advocacy, and collective bargaining, MNA empowers nurses to use a strong, collective voice to promote the profession of nursing and build safer workplaces for themselves, their patients and for healthy communities.

The function of MNA includes supporting and promoting the profession of nursing, fostering high standards of nursing practice, education and research, and to advocate for human rights, including patient rights. MNA offers continuing education opportunities that address relevant healthcare issues and assist nurses in fulfilling licensing requirements. Through collective bargaining, MNA has achieved some of the best contracts in the state and nation. And through advocacy, MNA brings the voices of nurses to our elected officials to influence changes that benefit patients, families, communities, and the profession of nursing.

MNA is dedicated to education of nurses through its continuing education initiatives. By working in partnership with community agencies, colleges & universities, and state level workgroups, MNA prepares, curates, and delivers timely, evidence-based education to all nurses and health professionals through a variety of formats and settings.

MNA's collective bargaining addresses economic issues such as pay and benefits and nursing practice issues such as scope of practice and safety in the workplace. MNA nurses have negotiated contracts to eliminate mandatory overtime, set safe and appropriate nurse-to-patient staffing ratios, reduce exposure to hazardous conditions, and provide for protections during the COVID-19 pandemic.

On the state and federal levels, MNA advocates for bipartisan laws to establish safe nurse-to-patient ratios, limit forced overtime, and require hospital transparency. MNA also advocates for legislation to prevent workplace violence against nurses and other health care workers.

MNA is an affiliate of the National Nurses United and of the AFL-CIO.

MI NURSES
Association

www.minurses.org
888.MI.NURSE 517.349.5640

Standards and regulatory mechanisms are subject to change.
Readers are advised to continually update their resources on legal and professional regulations.

ISBN   978-0-9634643-2-3

EDITORS

Carissa Miller, PhD, RN, MSN, CNE, CNS
MNA Associate Executive Director of Nursing Education, Practice & Research and Government Affairs

ie Lott, RN, MSN
MNA Accredited Provider Program Director & Community Liaison

nn Kettering Sincox
MNA Project and Publications Director

an Myckowiak
MNA Legislative and Political Program Coordinator

amie Bissel
MNA Attorney

awn Kettinger
MNA Government Affairs Director

ick Yorke
MNA Attorney

GRAPHIC DESIGN
llied Printing
over designed using resources from Freepik.com
and photo created by rawpixel.com

MI NURSES Association

**PROFESSIONAL
& LEGAL
REGULATION OF
NURSING PRACTICE
IN MICHIGAN**

5TH EDITION

FOREWORD

It is my pleasure to introduce the 5th edition of Professional and Legal Regulation of Nursing Practice in Michigan Handbook, 2021. This guide serves as great resource for both student nurses and licensed nurses currently practicing in the state of Michigan. Michigan is unique in that it does not have a Nurse Practice Act to guide nurses. Instead, we have a consolidated practice act that covers 26 health occupations called the Occupational Regulation Sections of the Michigan Public Health Code, PA 368 of 1978.

In Michigan, there are specific rules and responsibilities that are detailed in the Public Health Code that govern the profession and licensure of nursing. This handbook details those along with the standards of nursing and professional practice. Also covered is a section on workplace rights and the importance of protecting yourself. Users will find this handbook gives information on several areas of adversity or challenges that will affect their practice, should the need occur.

Registered nurses may delegate tasks to others: contained in this handbook you will find information on what you legally can and cannot delegate. Your Michigan nursing license is dependent on knowing and practicing within these regulations. Michigan nurses are licensed for two years and information on requirements for renewal is also included.

I want to thank the nurses and staff involved in putting together this updated edition. Healthcare regulations are constantly changing and the Michigan Nurses Association works diligently along with National Nurses United to bring current nursing practice information to you. This handbook is a reflection of some of the many resources the Michigan Nurses Association has available to all nurses.

As a nurse, you have chosen one of the most challenging yet rewarding careers. For the past 19 years, nursing has ranked number one as the most honest and ethical profession in Gallup's annual poll. With the trust of the public behind us, we need to use our voices in solidarity to stand strong to provide safe patient care and to protect our practice. As you journey along your nursing career path, there will be many options for you to choose. I urge you to mentor those just learning, stand firm in promoting safe patient care and work with other nurses to improve healthcare and provide quality outcomes for those that have put their trust in you. Seize the opportunities that nursing will present to you and know that every day that you practice, you will make a difference in someone's life!

Diane Goddeeris

Diane Goddeeris, RN, BSN

MNA Executive Director 2020

National Nurses United Vice President 2009-2012

Michigan Nurses Association President 2007-2009

Staff Nurse-Sparrow Hospital, Lansing, Michigan 1980-2018

TABLE OF CONTENTS

NTRODUCTION

Nursing, like other professions, functions within a system of public and private checks and balances. These include professional regulation (private domain), government regulation (public domain), and judicial determination (public domain).

The primary legal regulatory mechanism for nursing is state licensure which is created through legislative statute and administrative rules. Through state government, the Legislature and state departments establish laws and rules that represent minimum standards of practice for registered nurses. Government policy is also stimulated, changed or interpreted by actions within the judicial system. The resulting framework of law, rules and court interpretation makes up the legal regulatory mechanism for nursing.

A prime underpinning for regulation or judicial determinations is the presence of standards of practice developed by the respective professions. The American Nurses Association (ANA) has long assumed the responsibility for developing and maintaining the scope of practice statement and standards that apply to the practice of all professional nurses and that serve as a template for evaluation of nursing specialty practice. Both the scope and standards, however, belong to the profession and thus require broad input into their development and revision.

"Practice standards must be developed by nurses and grounded in nursing's ethical commitments and developing body of knowledge. These standards must also reflect nursing's responsibility to society. Nursing identifies its own scope of practice as informed, specified, or directed by state and federal law and regulation, by relevant societal values, and by ANA's Code of Ethics for Nurses with Interpretive Statements and other foundation documents." (Code of Ethics Provision 7.2)

Since nurses practice within both a professional and a legal framework, it is imperative that an understanding is gained as to how these mechanisms affect individual scope of practice. *Professional & Legal Regulation of Nursing Practice in Michigan* will focus on the state regulatory agency, professional society responsibilities, and how nurses are held to established standards of practice.

Definition of Nursing

Nursing integrates the art and science of caring and focuses on the protection, promotion, and optimization of health and human functioning; prevention of illness and injury; facilitation of healing; and alleviation of suffering through compassionate presence. Nursing is the diagnosis and treatment of human responses and advocacy in the care of individuals, families, groups, communities, and populations in recognition of the connection of all humanity. - *Nursing Scope and Standards of Practice, Fourth Edition (2021)*

Scope of Nursing Practice

The American Nurses Association (2021) defines the Scope of Nursing Practice as:
the who, what, where, when, why, and how of nursing practice and roles. Each of these questions must be answered to provide a complete picture of the dynamic and complex practice of nursing and its membership and evolving boundaries.

The definition of nursing provides a succinct characterization of the "what" of nursing. All registered nurses, including those identified as graduate level prepared nurses or advanced practice registered nurses, comprise the "who" constituency and have been educated, titled, and maintain active licensure to practice nursing. Nursing occurs "when there is a need for nursing knowledge, wisdom, caring, leadership, practice, or education, anytime, anywhere. Nursing occurs whenever there is a need for nursing knowledge, wisdom, caring, leadership, practice, or education, anytime, anywhere. Nursing occurs in any environment "where" there is a healthcare consumer in need of care, information, or advocacy. The "how" of nursing practice is defined as the ways, means, methods, and manners that nurses use to practice professionally. The "why" is characterized as nursing's response to the changing needs of society to achieve positive healthcare consumer outcomes in keeping with nursing's social contract with an obligation to society. The depth and breadth in which individual registered nurses engage in the total scope of nursing practice are dependent on their education, experience, role, and the population served. Formal periodic review and revision of the scope of nursing practice statement ensures a contemporary description of nursing practice is in place (ANA, 2021).

Standards of Nursing Practice

he American Nurses Association (2021) describes the eighteen Standards of Professional Nursing Practice in 1e following terms:

...authoritative statements of the actions and behaviors that all registered nurses, regardless of role, population, specialty, and setting, are expected to perform competently. These published standards may serve as evidence of the standard of practice, with the understanding that the application of the standards and accompanying competencies depends on contest, circumstances, or situation.

The standards are subject to change with the dynamics of the nursing profession as evidence is discovered and new patterns of professional practice are developed and accepted by the nursing profession and the public. In addition, specific conditions and clinical circumstances may also affect the application of the standards at a given time, such as during a natural disaster, epidemic, or pandemic. The standards are subject to formal, periodic review and revision (ANA, 2021).

he standards are categorized into two groupings: Standards of Practice and Standards of Professional *ractice. Various competencies define the roles and actions of the registered nurse for each standard. More pecific competencies are outlined for graduate-level prepared nurses and advanced practice nurses (APRNs) *ithin each standard.

Standards of Practice

The Standards of Practice listed outline a proficient level of nursing care as proved by the critical thinking model known as the nursing process, which involves the actions of assessment, diagnosis, outcomes identification, planning, implementation, and evaluation. "The nursing process encompasses significant actions taken by registered nurses and forms the foundation of the nurse's decision-making, practice, and provision of care" (American Nurses Association, 2021).

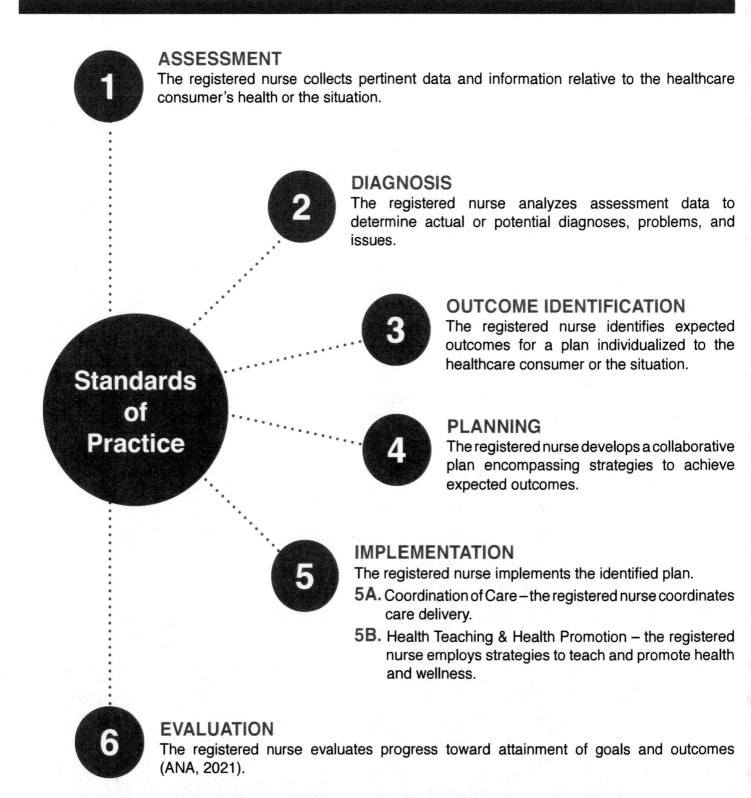

1 **ASSESSMENT**
The registered nurse collects pertinent data and information relative to the healthcare consumer's health or the situation.

2 **DIAGNOSIS**
The registered nurse analyzes assessment data to determine actual or potential diagnoses, problems, and issues.

3 **OUTCOME IDENTIFICATION**
The registered nurse identifies expected outcomes for a plan individualized to the healthcare consumer or the situation.

4 **PLANNING**
The registered nurse develops a collaborative plan encompassing strategies to achieve expected outcomes.

5 **IMPLEMENTATION**
The registered nurse implements the identified plan.
5A. Coordination of Care – the registered nurse coordinates care delivery.
5B. Health Teaching & Health Promotion – the registered nurse employs strategies to teach and promote health and wellness.

6 **EVALUATION**
The registered nurse evaluates progress toward attainment of goals and outcomes (ANA, 2021).

Standards of Practice

Standards of Professional Practice

The standards listed describe a proficient level of behavior by the registered nurse in the professional role. All registered nurses are accountable for their professional actions to themselves, their healthcare consumers, their peers, and, ultimately, to society.

Revisions to the Standards of Professional Practice by the American Nurses Association in 2021 included the addition of a new standard for Advocacy and advancements to the previously titled standard of "Culturally Congruent Practice."

In adopting a standard for Advocacy, ANA seeks to address and eliminate passive acceptance of the status quo within the profession and practice settings. Advocacy requires deposing rigid thinking and movement toward a culture of exploring creative solutions.

The Standard "Respectful and Equitable Practice" replaces the previous standard "Culturally Congruent Practice" and encompasses the principles of respect, equity, inclusion, and social justice. This revised standard dismisses the idea that nurses should be culturally competent; rather, nurses should strive for cultural humility, in which they display respect for individuals and cultures different from their own, while challenging their own biases that could impact nursing interactions in a pejorative manner. Learning and unlearning should be a continuous journey rather than a destination when working within the framework of cultural humility.

By evolving this standard, ANA seeks to highlight the nurse's obligation to eliminate avoidable suffering, which occurs due to lack of respect for others "manifested by dysfunctional processes and inherent biases embedded within the systems of care" (ANA, 2021, p. 22). ANA articulates that nonjudgmental care is required to eliminate avoidable suffering and cannot be practiced in a way that is forced while simply suppressing personal biases during patient interactions. Such actions are major contributing factors to the inequities of care and health disparities ever present in our modern American society (ANA, 2021).

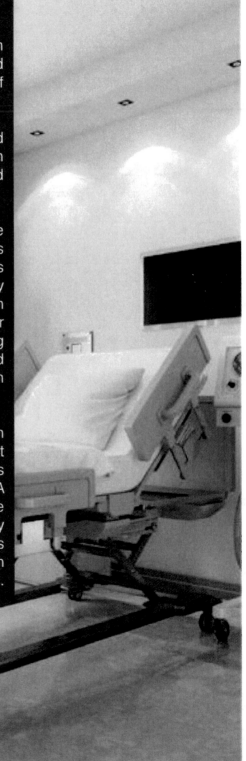

7 **ETHICS**
The registered nurse integrates ethic in all aspects of practice.

8* **ADVOCACY**
The registered nurse demonstrates advocacy in all roles and settings.

9* **RESPECTFUL AND EQUITABLE PRACTICE**
The registered nurse practices with cultural humility and inclusiveness.

Standards of Practice

10 **COMMUNICATION**
The registered nurse communicates effectively in all areas of professional practice.

11 **COLLABORATION**
The registered nurse collaborates with the healthcare consumer and other key stakeholders.

12 **LEADERSHIP**
The registered nurse leads within the profession and practice setting.

13

EDUCATION
The registered nurse seeks knowledge and competence that reflects current nursing practice and promotes futuristic thinking.

14

SCHOLARLY INQUIRY
The registered nurse integrates scholarship, evidence, and research findings into practice.

15

QUALITY OF PRACTICE
The registered nurse contributes to quality nursing practice.

Standards of Practice

16

PROFESSIONAL PRACTICE EVALUATION
The registered nurse evaluates one's own and others' nursing practice.

17

RESOURCE STEWARDSHIP
The registered nurse utilized appropriate resources to plan, provide, and sustain evidence-based nursing services that are safe, effective, and financially responsible and used judiciously.

18

ENVIRONMENTAL HEALTH
The registered nurse practices in a manner that advances environmental safety and health. (ANA, 2021)

new or revised standard

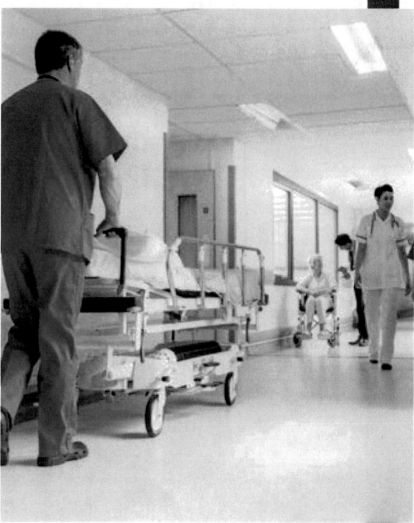

Code of Ethics for Nurses:
American Nurses Association

Ethics, or the moral principles that govern behavior, are essential to the practice of nursing, whose core service is to the dignity and well-being of the human person. As such, the Code of Ethics for Nurses serves as an outline for ethical professional nursing practice. According to the American Nurses Association (2021), the provisions in the Code of Ethics for Nurses establish the following:

- Addresses the nurse's fundamental values and commitments, accountability and duties to self and others, and aspects of obligations at the professional and societal levels.
- Provides direction in addressing ethical issues that arise at the clinical, organizational, and societal levels.

Code of Ethics for Nurses

The Code of Ethics for Nurses consists of nine provisions:

Provision 1

The nurse practices with compassion and respect for the inherent dignity, worth, and unique attributes of every person.

Provision 2

The nurse's primary commitment is to the patient, whether an individual, family, group, community, or population.

Provision 3

The nurse promotes, advocates for, and protects the rights, health and safety of the patient.

Provision 4

The nurse has authority, accountability, and responsibility for nursing practice; makes decisions; and takes action consistent with the obligation to promote health and to provide optimal care.

Provision 5

The nurse owes the same duties to self as to others, including the responsibility to promote health and safety, preserve wholeness of character and integrity, maintain competence, and continue personal and professional growth.

Provision 6

The nurse, through individual and collective effort, establishes, maintains, and improves the ethical environment of the work setting and conditions of employment that are conducive to safe, quality health care.

Provision 7

The nurse, in all roles and settings, advances the profession through research and scholarly inquiry, professional standards development, and the generation of both nursing and health policy.

Provision 8

The nurse collaborates with other health professionals and the public to protect human rights, promote health diplomacy, and reduce health disparities.

Provision 9

The profession of nursing, collectively through its professional organizations, must articulate nursing values, maintain the integrity of the profession, and integrate principles of social justice into nursing and health policy.

LEGAL REGULATION OF NURSING PRACTICE

Michigan Government

State government plays a vital role in ensuring that nursing maintains appropriate standards of patient care. The legislative branch establishes laws, the judicial branch applies and interprets the laws, and the executive branch provides the administrative structure to enforce the laws.

Governmental regulation, however, sets only minimum standards. It is up to nursing professionals individually and collectively to encourage the highest standards within nursing practice and the profession.

Legislative Branch

The Michigan Senate and the Michigan House of Representatives:

- establish laws that protect the health and safety of Michigan residents;
- provide oversight for the budget process for all spending;
- administer the process that creates rules that implement laws; and,
- create special committees and task forces that may deal with health-related issues.

All of these duties directly affect how nurses are educated, become licensed, are disciplined and carry out their daily practice.

Judicial Branch

Courts interpret and apply laws, rules and regulations. These interpretations impact nursing practice in many of the same ways as the legislative branch, since courts often decide, for example, what constitutes malpractice, what penalties apply, and who is qualified or not qualified to practice nursing.

Executive Branch

The executive branch of Michigan government includes many departments, bureaus and agencies. The purpose of these entities is to protect the health and welfare of Michigan residents. Nursing practice is affected by the programs and services created by these and other divisions of state government. (Michigan Legislature, 2021)

The Michigan Department of Health and Human Services (MDHHS)

The role of MDHHS is to oversee the health and safety of the public of Michigan with particular attention to providing for the needs of vulnerable and under-served populations and those with chronic medical conditions. MDHHS focuses on creating a healthier Michigan so that its residents may realize their fullest health potential and enjoy productive lives.

Services are planned and delivered through these integrated components:

- Chronic disease and injury control
- The Bureau of Disease Control, Prevention and Epidemiology
- Primary care and public health, including assistance for those with limited incomes
- Health statistics and reports (MDHHS, 2021)

Michigan Department of Licensing and Regulatory Affairs (LARA)

The mission of the Michigan Department of Licensing and Regulatory Affairs (LARA) is to support business growth and job creation while safeguarding Michigan's residents through a simple, fair, efficient and transparent regulatory structure (Licensing and Regulatory Affairs, 2021).

Within LARA, the Bureau of Professional Licensing (BPL) includes the Enforcement Division, Licensing Division, and Investigations & Inspections Division. BPL is responsible for licensing and regulating over 700,000 individuals who are regulated by either the Michigan Occupational Code or the Public Health Code. BPL is also responsible for maintaining the Health Professional Recovery Program (HPRP), and the Michigan Automated Prescription System (MAPS) (Licensing and Regulatory Affairs, 2021).

The Licensing Division, in conjunction with state licensing boards, regulates 26 health professions in Michigan under the Michigan Public Health Code. This division is responsible for providing customer service, pre-licensure support and application processing. The Licensing Division fulfills several functions such as reviewing applications; processing renewals; issuing licenses, registrations, and/or certificates; and maintaining all licensing records for over 700,000 professionals (Licensing and Regulatory Affairs, 2021). The Licensing Division is also responsible for determining eligibility for examination and licensure, monitoring licensee's compliance with continuing education requirements, and providing administrative support to the boards. In addition, the division oversees administration of examinations to those professions that have an examination requirement. This is the division that oversees licensing for professional registered nurses (RNs), licensed practical nurses (LPNs) and advanced practice registered nurses (APRNs); and includes the Michigan Board of Nursing.

Other functions of the Licensing Division:

- Mails licenses
- Randomly audits nursing continuing education contact hours
- Collects licensing fees
- Investigates activities related to the practice of nursing by a licensed nurse, or an applicant for licensure

■ Holds hearings and orders relevant testimony to be taken
■ Reports findings from hearings to the Board of Nursing (Licensing and Regulatory Affairs, 2021).

Michigan Public Health Code

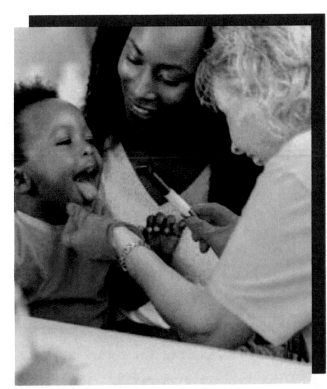

...fore 1978, Michigan law directing nursing practice ...as found in a Nurse Practice Act. In 1978, the Michigan ...gislature combined all laws regulating health personnel ...to one statute consolidating the legal framework for ...rsing resulting in the Michigan Public Health Code (Public ...ct [PA] 368), rather than in a separate Nurse Practice Act. ...e Michigan Public Health Code is a compilation of laws ...tended to protect and promote the health and well-being ... Michigan's residents. It is a far-reaching set of laws that ...pacts every aspect of health care, including nursing. It ...ts minimum standards that must be maintained and ...fines enforcement procedures and penalties for those ...ho do not comply.

...is approach is unique to Michigan since most states still ...ovide separate laws for each of the health occupations ...ch as a Nurse Practice Act. The Michigan Public Health Code addresses issues of licensure, specialty ...rtification, educational programs, discipline, delegation, and authority to practice.

...ue to this Michigan Public Health Code structure versus a Nurse Practice Act, Michigan currently does not ...articipate in the National Council of the State Boards of Nursing (NCSBN) which compiles and reports on ...ultiple states' Nurse Practice Act related data (NCSBN, 2021).

Why was the Public Health Code (PA 368) developed?

...he purpose of combining laws was to coordinate and articulate most aspects of the state government's ...gulatory responsibility for the public health of its residents.

... portion of the Occupational Regulation Sections of the Michigan Public Health Code contains definitions, ...eneral provisions and regulations applicable to all licensed or registered health occupations and to the health ...ccupation boards that govern them.

...he general portion of the Public Health Code is followed by sections that are specific to each of the health ...ccupations (Michigan Legislature, 2021).

What parts of the Public Health Code are important to understand?

...he general definitions and provisions in Article 15 (Health Occupations), as well as those which refer specifically ... nursing (Part 172), should be considered in their totality if nurses, employers, and the public are to fully ...nderstand the broad legal parameters of nursing. The basic purpose of the code is to protect the health, safety, ...nd welfare of the public. (Michigan Legislature, 2021).

How is the Michigan Public Health Code implemented?

Once a law such as the Michigan Public Health Code is passed, it is implemented through a variety of actions, including:

Development of rules as required. Following the enactment of laws, the department or agency charged with implementing the law develops further specificity through administrative rules. Rules may not expand or contract the law, rather they serve to interpret or provide specificity in its application.

Administrative rules must go through a detailed procedure before they become effective. This procedure is designed to allow public participation and comment.

The procedure includes public hearings and a review by the Legislative Services Bureau and the Office of Regulatory Reform to ensure the legality of the proposed rule, and consideration by a joint committee of the Michigan Senate and House of Representatives. This Joint Committee on Administrative Rules may act to approve the rule, disapprove the rule or certify an impasse. After rules have been approved by the committee or by resolution of both houses of the legislature, the state may proceed to formally adopt the rule. Once adopted, rules have the effect of law (Michigan Legislature, 2021)

Michigan Board of Nursing:
The Foundation of Nursing in Michigan

The Michigan Public Health Code defines the practice of nursing in Michigan and empowers the Michigan Board of Nursing to establish qualifications for nurse licensure; establish standards for education and approve nurse education programs; develop and implement criteria for assurance of continued competency; and take disciplinary action against licensees when the health, safety, and welfare of the public has been adversely affected.

The Michigan Board of Nursing was originally created with the enactment of the Nurse Practice Act, Public Act 319 of 1909, and authority was transferred to the Nursing Practice Act of 1967 by Public Act 149 of 1967.

On September 30, 1978, authority was again transferred to the Public Health Code, Public Act 368 of 1978, as amended. On April 9, 2017, the Public Health Code was amended by Public Act 499 of 2017, to add a clinical nurse specialist to the Board (Michigan Legislature, 2021).

The Public Health Code permits LPN board members to act upon all matters except those related to standards for the education and training of RNs, and decisions on such matters are concurred in solely by a majority of the RN and public board members.

The Board of Nursing webpage can be found through the following link:
https://www.michigan.gov/lara/0,4601,7-154-89334_72600_72603_27529_27542---,00.html

Throughout this document, sections of Michigan Public Health Code and its Acts will appear verbatim.

Who is on the Michigan Board of Nursing?

As the Michigan Public Health Code established the creation of the Board of Nursing, it also stipulated the number and qualifications of its members.

Part 172 Nursing, Sec. 333.17221 Michigan Board of Nursing; creation; number and qualifications of members.

The Michigan Board of Nursing shall consist of the following 24 voting members who shall meet the requirements of part 161: 9 registered professional nurses, 1 nurse midwife, 1 nurse anesthetist, 1 nurse practitioner, 1 clinical nurse specialist, 3 licensed practical nurses, and 8 public members. Three of the registered professional nurse members shall be engaged in nursing education, 1 of whom shall be in less than a baccalaureate program, 1 in a baccalaureate or higher program and 1 in a licensed practical nurse program and each of whom shall have a master's degree from an accredited college with a major in nursing. Three of the registered professional nurse members shall be engaged in nursing practice or nursing administration, each of whom shall have a baccalaureate degree in nursing from an accredited college. Three of the registered professional nurse members shall be engaged in nursing practice or nursing administration, each of whom shall be a non-baccalaureate registered nurse. The 3 licensed practical nurse members shall have graduated from a state approved program for the preparation of individuals to practice as licensed practical nurses. The nurse midwife, the nurse anesthetist, the nurse practitioner, and the clinical nurse specialist shall each have a specialty certification granted by the Michigan Board of Nursing in his or her respective specialty field (Michigan Legislature, 2021).

What does the Michigan Board of Nursing do?

The Board of Nursing meets six times per year. Meetings are open to the public.

Functions of the Board of Nursing:

- Grant licenses to RNs and LPNs
- Impose disciplinary action on licensees when the health, safety and welfare of the public has been adversely affected
- Establish standards for education and approve education programs
- Grant certification of specialties: nurse practitioners, nurse midwives, nurse anesthetists
- Generate/update administrative rules concurrent with the Michigan Public Health Code and Amendments
- Review test items for National Council Licensing Examination (NCLEX) (LARA, 2021)

Administrative Rules of the Michigan Board of Nursing

In addition to the Public Health Code, Michigan Board of Nursing Administrative Rules also provide the framework under which the Board of Nursing functions. Following are the Michigan Board of Nursing Administrative Rules, General Provisions 338.10101, which define certain terms used in these rules that appear in this publication.

Administrative Rules: Nursing Education Programs

A primary responsibility of the Michigan Board of Nursing is to establish standards for nursing schools and to approve Michigan nursing schools that meet those standards. The standards are laid out in a set of Administrative Rules (filed April 6, 2020) which can be accessed in full text from the Department of Licensing and Regulatory Affairs (LARA) website:

https://www.michigan.gov/lara/0,4601,7-154-89334_72600_72603_27529_27542---,00.html

Rule 101 (R 338.10101) Definitions.

(1) As used in this part:
  a. "Authorized representative" means the chairperson, vice chairperson, or such other member of the board or staff as the board may formally designate.
  b. "Board" means the Michigan Board of Nursing.
  c. "Code" means 1978 PA 368, MCL 333.1101 to 333.25211.
  d. "Department" means the Michigan department of licensing and regulatory affairs
(2) Terms defined in the act have the same meanings when used in these rules

The first rules outline the process and procedure for agencies to receive ***initial approval*** by the Board of Nursing to establish a program of nursing education. During the initial approval process, agencies must outline the intent, mission, and need for the program and provide evidence of financial support to establish security of the program and its students for a five-year period (see Rule 303 for more details). Following initial approval, the program can then receive ***full program approval*** after graduation of the second cohort but shall apply no later than graduation of the fourth cohort. Fully approved programs must receive ***accreditation*** by one of the following National accrediting bodies within outlined time-frames set forth in Rule 303d: Accreditation Commission for Education in Nursing (ACEN), Commission for Nursing Education Accreditation (CNEA), Commission on Collegiate Nursing Education (CCNE). The accreditation process requires nursing programs to perform a self-study of their processes and structures and provide a detailed report to the Board of Nursing as well as the accrediting agency of its findings, including NCLEX pass rates, admission, and retention rates. A review of the program by the accrediting body to ensure compliance with national standards typically happens on a 4-year cycle.

Rule 303 (R 338.10303) Initial program approval; procedure.

The following requirements are established for initial approval of a program of nursing education:

(a) The sponsoring agency shall submit all of the following to the board:

  (i) A letter of intent to initiate a program of nursing education.

  (ii) A feasibility study that clearly demonstrates all of the following, with supporting documentation relative to the proposed program location: (A) Need for the program. (B) Need for graduates of the proposed program. (C) Availability of students. (D) Impact on all existing nursing education programs in a 50-mile radius of the proposed program. (E) Ability of proposed clinical education sites to provide students with clinical experiences that meet course outcomes, provide students the opportunity to practice skills with individuals or groups across the life span and meet the requirements of R 338.10307(5), (6), (7), and (8). Evidence must also include documentation of the effect on other schools utilizing the proposed clinical facilities and letters of intent from the proposed clinical education sites, signed by the chief nursing officer, or an equivalent position, outlining the plan to accommodate all of the sponsoring agency's students.

(iii) Evidence that the mission of the sponsoring agency is consistent with the philosophy and purpose of a program to prepare students for the practice of nursing as defined in section 17201(1)(c) of the code, MCL 333.17201.

(iv) Evidence that the sponsoring agency will provide funding and other support for the nursing education program that meets all of the following requirements:

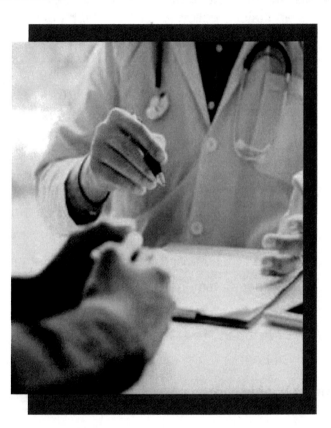

    (A) A 5-year budget in which the first 2 years of the budget do not include tuition and the remaining 3 years of the budget includes tuition.

    (B) A financial statement prepared by an independent certified public accountant or auditor, a bank line of credit, or a surety bond that equals the total tuition for all students who have been enrolled for 2 years.

    (C) Submission of evidence that the sponsoring agency will provide appropriate physical facilities and other support services for the nursing education program, in conjunction with other departments in the sponsoring agency, including faculty, administration, and student participation in governance of the sponsoring agency, a grievance or complaint process, counseling, academic advising, career placement, financial aid, and learning resource centers or library.

(v) Evidence of approval to provide financial aid for students, under Title IV of the Higher Education Act of 1965, 20 USC 1070 et seq.

(vi) A sponsoring agency that is an institution requiring approval from the department's proprietary schools' unit, or its successor agency, to conduct a nursing education program or to confer a particular degree or certificate upon the graduates of the program shall submit to the board a copy of the approval. A proprietary school shall possess a state-issued license, be in operation for 2 years, offer health-related courses, and demonstrate student success by certifying that exam results meet or exceed state or national averages.

(vii) Proposed number of students to be enrolled in the program annually, the number of times that enrollment periods will be held per year, and the dates when enrollment periods will be held annually.

(viii) Proposed first date of admission of students to the nursing sequence of the program.

(ix) Plans to recruit and employ a program director and other faculty members sufficiently in advance of admitting students to the nursing sequence to ensure consistency in the planning and implementation of the curriculum. If already appointed, the names and qualifications of the director of the program and other faculty members must be provided.

(x) The sponsoring agency shall provide evidence of a tuition policy in which students pay as they proceed through the program either by semesters, terms, units, or other time frame as specified by the sponsoring agency. The sponsoring agency shall also provide evidence of a refund policy that adheres to the refund policies of applicable state, federal, and accrediting agencies.

(xi) Evidence that students possess the necessary prerequisite education before admissions to the program. The program shall not be the provider of the prerequisite education, unless it is a state-approved higher educational institution or has the approval of the state to offer prerequisite courses.

(xii) A student contract or enrollment application that outlines the nursing education program's admission requirements, a tuition refund policy that complies with paragraph (x) of this subdivision, a withdrawal and failure policy, and academic progression and program completion requirements.

(xiii) History of sponsoring agency.

(b) Following initial approval from the board and before admitting the first cohort, the program director shall submit a self-study report to be approved by the board. The report must set forth evidence of plans for and compliance with the following:

(i) History of sponsoring agency.

(ii) Philosophy.

(iii) Conceptual framework.

(iv) Curriculum to include end of program student learning outcomes and course student learning outcomes.

(v) Course descriptions and outlines.

(vi) Signed clinical contracts or letters of commitment for clinical placements.

(vii) Evaluation methods and tools.

(viii) Program outcomes.

(ix) Director and faculty credentials.

(x) Student policies and support services.

(c) The board shall require a site visit to the program by a board-approved nurse site reviewer. The report of the site visit must be prepared by the nurse site reviewer and provided to the board and the sponsoring agency.

(d) After the first cohort has been admitted and during the initial approval period, the program director shall submit an annual nursing education program report to the board. The nursing education program report must include information about each of the following:

(i) Admission, progression, and retention of students.

(ii) Student achievement on the required licensure NCLEX examination.

(iii) Systematic program evaluation results, including, but not limited to, student evaluations, faculty reviews, NCLEX evaluation results, and attrition rates.

(iv) Program changes.

Rule 303a (R 338.10303a) Full program approval; procedure.

(1) The sponsoring agency may apply to the board for full approval of the program after graduation of the second cohort but shall apply no later than graduation of the fourth cohort. The sponsoring agency shall comply with the following requirements for full approval of a nursing education program:

(a) The sponsoring agency may apply to the board in the form of a letter.

(b) The sponsoring agency shall submit a final program approval report to the board. The report must provide an update of the self-study that was submitted for initial approval pursuant to R 338.10303(b), review the program's progress since initial approval was granted, and include a review and evaluation of program implementation.

(c) The board may require a subsequent site visit to the program by a board-approved nurse site reviewer before considering full approval. If conducted, a report of the site visit must be prepared by the nurse site reviewer and provided to the board and the sponsoring agency.

) NCLEX scores for the program up to the point of application of full approval must equate to the passage rates as required in R 338.10310.

) If by the end of the fourth cohort, a program does not satisfy the criteria for full approval set forth in this rule or has failed to apply for full approval as required under this rule, the board may begin the evaluation process of the program pursuant to section 17242 of the code, MCL 333.17242 and R 338.10310. (4) When granted full approval for the program of nursing education, the sponsoring agency shall continue to meet all of the requirements of this part.

Rule 303b (R 338.10303b) Continued program approval; requirements.

) After full approval has been granted under R 338.10303a, a sponsoring agency shall submit a comprehensive self-study report every 8 years for a non-accredited program or at the designated reporting times directed by the national accrediting organization for accredited programs. The report must include all of the following information for all of the years since the last self-study report was approved by the board.

(a) History of sponsoring agency.

(b) Philosophy.

(c) Conceptual framework.

(d) Curriculum to include end of program student learning outcomes and course student learning outcomes.

(e) Course descriptions and outlines.

(f) Signed clinical contracts or letters of commitment for clinical placements.

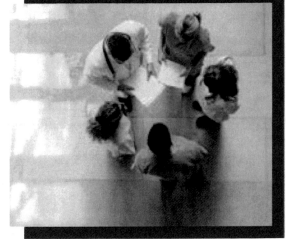

(g) Evaluation methods and tools.

(h) Program outcomes.

(i) Director and faculty credentials.

(j) Student policies and support services.

) A program may submit a letter of accreditation or reaccreditation from a nationally recognized accrediting organization of nursing education programs instead of a self-study report prepared for the board. The schedule for submission of a self-study report for accredited programs must follow the schedule of the nationally recognized accrediting organization. The accreditation letter must include documentation of decisions and recommendations from the accrediting organization and be submitted to the board within 1 month following receipt of the nationally recognized accrediting organization's decision on accreditation of the nursing education program. The board may request further documentation regarding accreditation from the sponsoring agency. Programs that have accreditation date changes shall notify the board of nursing to determine a submission date.

(3) After a program has been granted full approval under R 338.10303a, the sponsoring agency shall submit a nurse education program report to the board every 4 years for a non-accredited program or at the midpoint of the accreditation cycle for nationally accredited programs. The nursing education program report must include all of the following information for all of the years since the last self-study report was approved by the board:

(a) Admission, progression, and retention of students.

(b) Student achievement on the required licensure NCLEX examination.

(c) Systematic program evaluation results and action plan, including but not limited to, student evaluations, faculty reviews, NCLEX evaluation results, and attrition rates.

(d) Program changes.

(e) Faculty qualifications, assignments, and any faculty exceptions.

(4) The board shall notify the program director of the date by which a nursing education program report must be submitted.

Rule 303c (R 338.10303c) Program changes; requirements.

(1) A major program change means any of the following:

(a) Revision of the program's philosophy, conceptual framework, curriculum, program outcomes, student learning outcomes, or changes that increase the use of simulation more than 10% of the total clinical hours in a program.

(b) Change in primary instruction delivery methods.

(c) Elimination of separate course content for an integrated approach.

(d) A permanent expansion in the number of students served.

(e) Increase or decrease in overall program credits.

(f) Providing the theory portion of the curriculum at an additional location that is separate from the primary campus using the same curriculum as the primary campus. Initial approval under R 338.10303 must be obtained if anything other than theory is taught at the additional location.

(2) A nursing education program shall submit major program changes to the board in writing and the major program changes must be approved by the board before implementation. All of the following information must be submitted when requesting approval of a major program change:

(a) A comparative description of the current and proposed program or portion of the program which is proposed for change.

(b) Rationale for the change.

(c) Plans to evaluate the effect of the change.

(d) Documents evidencing support for the requested change.

(3) A minor program change means a change that does not permanently affect the program's philosophy, conceptual framework, program outcomes, student learning outcomes, approved enrollment numbers, increase simulation experiences by more than 10%, change the primary instruction delivery methods, eliminate a separate course content for an integrated approach, permanently expand the number of students served, or increase or decrease the overall program credits.

4) A nursing education program shall submit minor program changes to the board in writing before implementation. Minor program changes include, but are not limited to, all of the following:

  (a) Changing prerequisites, co-requisites, or both.

  (b) A temporary expansion of students. After 1 year, if the program desires to make the temporary increase in seats permanent, a major program change must be submitted pursuant to subrule (1) of this rule.

  (c) Separation of 1 course into 2 courses.

  (d) Moving a course from 1 semester to another.

  (e) Combining 2 courses.

  (f) Changing the sequence in which courses are offered.

5) A nursing education program shall submit all of the following information if requesting approval of a minor program change:

  (a) A comparative description of the current and proposed program or portion of the program that is proposed for change.

  (b) Rationale for the change.

  (c) Plans to evaluate the effect of the change.

6) If a program closure occurs, the department may grant a temporary seat increase to another program to assist displaced students if the following criteria are met:

  (a) Additional seats that are needed are identified.

  (b) Documentation that there is sufficient faculty on staff to handle the increase in students is provided.

  (c) Documentation that there is sufficient classroom and laboratory space to handle the increase in students is provided.

  (d) Documentation from clinical sites that they can handle the increase of students in the program is provided.

7) The type of program approval, initial or full, under which a program is conducted, shall not be altered when program changes are approved.

Rule 303d (R 338.10303d) Accreditation.

1) A nursing education program approved by the board shall be accredited pursuant to 1 of the following:

  (a) A nursing education program that has received full board approval pursuant to R 338.10303a, before the promulgation of this rule, shall receive nursing accreditation by a board-recognized nursing accreditation organization no later than January 1, 2025.

  (b) A nursing education program that has initial approval of the board shall receive nursing accreditation by a board-recognized nursing accreditation organization within 6 years of receiving full program approval pursuant to R 338.10303a.

  (c) A nursing education program that fails to achieve nursing accreditation by a board- recognized nursing accreditation organization as set forth by this rule shall be removed from the list of approved programs pursuant to section 17242 of the code, MCL 333.17242.

2) The board recognizes the following nursing education accrediting agencies or their successor organizations:

  (a) Accreditation Commission for Education in Nursing (ACEN).

  (b) Commission for Nursing Education Accreditation (CNEA).

(c) Commission on Collegiate Nursing Education (CCNE).

(3) Failure to maintain accreditation from an approved national nursing accrediting organization shall result in withdrawal of school approval pursuant to section 17242 of the code, MCL 333.17242, and R 338.10311. (State of Michigan, 2020).

Standards for *faculty* and *curriculum requirements* within a nursing program are outlined in Rules 305, 307, and 309. The Board of Nursing has established minimum degree requirements for program directors, as well as faculty teaching in the clinical and didactic settings. The most current rules establish that faculty teaching clinical must hold a minimum of a Bachelor of Science in Nursing (BSN) and those teaching didactic must hold a minimum of a Master of Science in Nursing (MSN). The rules also outline that each nursing faculty may precept a maximum of 8 students in the clinical setting. The rules for curriculum requirements help to ensure cohesion in content and preparation for the NCLEX across all nursing programs within the state.

Rule 305 (R 338.10305) Registered professional nurse and licensed practical nurse programs; program requirements; generally.

Programs of registered professional nursing education and licensed practical nursing education shall meet all of the following requirements:

(a) Comply with the curriculum requirements established by the board and with other requirements set forth in this part.

(b) Contribute to the safe practice of nursing by including the standards of practice, nursing behaviors, and other skills and knowledge in the curriculum to prepare students for the practice of nursing as defined in section 17201(1)(c) of the code, MCL 333.17201.

(c) Prepare students to meet the requirements for eligibility to take the required licensure NCLEX examination.

(d) Establish requirements for admission, progression, and graduation which must be made known and available in written form to prospective and current students.

(e) Establish a system for the permanent maintenance of course descriptions and student and graduate transcripts. R 338.10305a Registered professional nursing education program; program requirements; faculty requirements.

Rule 305a (R 338.10305a) Registered professional nursing education program; program requirements; faculty requirements.

(1) The program director and all nurse faculty members shall hold a current unrestricted license to practice as a registered professional nurse in this state.

(2) If clinical experiences are offered by the nursing education program at sites that are not located in this state, then any nurse faculty members at those sites shall hold a current unrestricted license to practice as a registered nurse in the state or Canadian province where the clinical experience is located.

(3) The program director shall hold a minimum of a graduate degree with a major in nursing. Written notification of a change in director must be provided to the board within 30 days and include a copy of the new director's curriculum vitae and school contact information.

(4) A member of the nursing faculty who provides didactic/theory instruction shall hold a minimum of a

graduate degree. The majority of the didactic/theory faculty shall hold a graduate degree with a major in nursing, unless an exception is granted under subrule (7) of this rule. If the graduate degree is not in nursing, the faculty member shall hold a minimum of a baccalaureate degree in nursing or an equivalent standing in a nationally nursing accredited Associate Degree in Nursing to Master's of Science in Nursing (ADN to MSN) nursing education program with attestation of baccalaureate level competency from that educational program. Courses that are non-nursing in content but are health-related are exempt from the requirements of this subrule and may be taught by non-nurse faculty.

) A member of the nursing faculty who provides instruction in either the clinical or simulation laboratory shall hold a minimum of a baccalaureate degree in nursing or an equivalent standing in a nationally nursing accredited ADN to MSN nursing education program with attestation of baccalaureate level competency from that educational program.

) Notwithstanding section 16148(6) of the code, MCL 333.16148, all nursing faculty shall meet the requirements of subrules (4) and (5) of this rule by January 6, 2022.

) An exception may be made to the requirements of subrule (4) of this rule for full- time or part-time nursing faculty and shall be based on the faculty member's progress toward meeting the requirements of these rules during each year for which the exception is requested. Board approval for faculty exception requests must be received before the faculty member begins course instruction. A maximum of 5 yearly exceptions shall be granted to any full-time or part-time faculty member.

) Nursing faculty shall be sufficient in number to prepare students to achieve the outcomes of the program. The maximum ratio of students to faculty in clinical areas involving direct care of patients must be not more than 8 students to 1 faculty member. The maximum ratio of students to faculty in clinical areas involving non-direct and precepted patient care must meet the clinical affiliate's guidelines and maintain patient and community safety.

Rule 305b (R 338.10305b) Licensed practical nursing education program; program requirements; faculty requirements

) The program director and all nurse faculty members shall hold a current unrestricted license to practice as a registered professional nurse in this state.

) If clinical experiences are offered by the nursing education program at sites that are not located in this state, then any nurse faculty members at those sites shall hold a current unrestricted license to practice as a registered professional nurse in the state or Canadian province where the clinical experience is located.

) The program director shall hold a minimum of a graduate degree in nursing. Written notification of a change in director must be provided to the board within 30 days and include a copy of the new director's curriculum vitae and school contact information.

) Every member of the nursing faculty shall hold a minimum of a baccalaureate degree in nursing, unless an exception is granted under subrule (6) of this rule. Courses that are non-nursing in content but are health-related are exempt from the requirements of this subrule and may be taught by non-nurse faculty.

) Notwithstanding section 16148(7) of the code, MCL 333.16148, all nursing faculty shall comply with the requirements of subrule (4) of this rule by January 6, 2022.

) An exception may be made to the requirements of subrule (4) of this rule for full- time or part-time nursing faculty and shall be based on the faculty member's progress toward meeting the requirements of these rules during each year for which the exception is requested. Board approval for faculty exception requests must be received before the faculty member begins course instruction. A maximum of 5 yearly exceptions shall be granted to any full-time or part-time faculty member.

(7) Nursing faculty shall be sufficient in number to prepare students to achieve the outcomes of the program. The maximum ratio of students to faculty in clinical areas involving direct care of patients must be not more than 8 students to 1 faculty member. The maximum ratio of students to faculty in clinical areas involving non-direct patient care must meet the clinical affiliate's guidelines and maintain patient and community safety.

Rule 305c (R 338.10305c) Registered professional nursing and licensed practical nursing education programs; preceptor requirements

(1) A program of nursing education that uses the personnel of a clinical facility as preceptors to facilitate the faculty-directed clinical experience of students to meet the requirements for an internship or to meet the clinical requirements in the capstone course, shall meet all of the following requirements:

(a) Each preceptor shall be approved by the faculty of the program of nursing education.

(b) Each preceptor shall possess a minimum of 1 year of clinical nursing experience and supervisor recommendation.

(c) Each preceptor shall hold an unencumbered license in the state where the clinical experience occurs.

(d) The faculty of the program of nursing education shall ensure that each preceptor is provided education including the roles and responsibilities of students, faculty members, and preceptors. The program shall maintain documentation of preceptor education.

(e) Before the preceptor begins instruction of the students, the faculty of the program of nursing shall develop written learning outcomes for the clinical experience and provide a copy of those outcomes to each preceptor.

(f) The faculty member shall retain authority and responsibility for the student's learning experiences and shall confer routinely and periodically with the preceptor and student to monitor and evaluate the learning experiences.

(g) The maximum ratio of precepted students to a supervising faculty member must be not more than 10 students to 1 faculty member.

(h) If the faculty member is not physically present in the area in which students are practicing, he or she shall be immediately available by telephone or other means of telecommunication when students are engaged in clinical activities with a preceptor.

(i) Preceptors shall not be used to replace clinical faculty in prelicensure certificate, associate, or baccalaureate degree nursing programs.

(j) A preceptor shall supervise not more than 1 student during any 1 scheduled work time or shift. This rule does not apply to staff nurses used by faculty intermittently during non-precepted clinical experiences.

Rule 307 (R 338.10307) Registered professional nursing and licensed practical nursing education programs; curriculum; organization, development, implementation, control, and evaluation

) The program director and faculty shall organize, develop, implement, control, and evaluate the curriculum on a regularly scheduled basis within the framework of the philosophy, purposes, and outcomes of the sponsoring agency and those approved by the board.

) The curriculum outcomes must identify the behavioral expectations of the graduate of the program and must be used for all of the following purposes:

  (a) Developing, organizing, implementing, and evaluating the curriculum.

  (b) Identifying outcomes for levels of progression and course and program completion.

  (c) Providing to the student an organized pattern to follow in which the sequence of learning is from the simple to the complex and from the known to the unknown, with each learning experience built on previously learned information of nursing and related scientific knowledge.

  (d) Organizing the courses to approximate, as closely as possible, the schedules of the sponsoring agency in terms, quarters, semesters, or trimesters.

  (e) Distributing the courses throughout the curriculum so that an unreasonable overload does not exist in any segment of the sequence.

) The philosophy and conceptual framework or rationale for the program must be the basis for the organization of the nursing content of the curriculum.

) The course content and other learning experiences must promote student growth in all of the following areas:

  (a) The understanding of the roles and responsibilities of the members of the nursing profession.

  (b) The application of the principles of nursing and the sciences which are basic to nursing practice in the development of plans of care for the patient or client.

  (c) The provision of direct and indirect nursing care.

  (d) The understanding of effective human relations and demonstrating the ability to use these principles in nursing situations.

  (e) The recognition of physical, psychosocial, and spiritual needs of diverse patient/client populations in the provision of nursing care.

  (f) The understanding of health, including the manifestations of disease and the initiation, organization, and application of the principles underlying the nursing care provided.

  (g) Developing skills and abilities in the administration of all aspects of nursing care using the nursing process, including all of the following:

    (i) Communications.

    (ii) Critical thinking, clinical reasoning, and problem solving.

    (iii) Understanding legal and professional responsibilities.

    (iv) Inter-professional relationships with other health care providers.

    (v) Evidence-based practice.

    (vi) Quality and safety.

  (h) Understanding and protecting the rights of patients or clients.

(5) All cooperating agencies selected for clinical laboratory and simulation laboratory experiences shall have standards of nursing care that demonstrate concern for the patient or client and evidence the skillful application of all measures of quality and safe, evidence-based nursing practice.

(6) All cooperating agencies shall have a current license, if required, for their operation and adhere to the local zoning ordinances governing their operation.

(7) When a nurse site reviewer visits a site, he or she may survey cooperating agencies as a part of the review process to determine the contribution each makes to the course and program outcomes. Selection must be made by the nurse site reviewer.

(8) Each resource selected to provide clinical experience shall indicate a willingness to cooperate in the curriculum by providing a letter of intent, a written agreement, or a formal contract. Each cooperating agency shall provide experiences of a quality and quantity that will enable all students to meet the outcomes established for the clinical experience pursuant to R 338.10303.

Rule 309 (R 338.10309) Licensed practical nursing education program; curriculum; implementation

(1) The director and faculty of a program of nursing education leading to licensure as a licensed practical nurse shall comply with all of the following provisions:

  (a) Select courses and ensure teaching concepts on which the theory and practice of practical nursing are based. The basic principles of the natural and applied sciences that are fundamental to the theory and practice of practical nursing and that are applied in the planning and implementation of nursing care must be included.

  (b) Provide courses and clinical and simulation laboratory experiences in the care of individuals across diverse age groups, genders, races and cultures, in medical, surgical, pediatric, obstetrical, and geriatric nursing and provide supervised practice in the administration of medications. Clinical laboratory, simulation laboratory, and clinical experience hours must be sufficient to meet the outcomes of the curriculum.

  (c) Ensure that courses include content relating to all of the following:

    (i) The legal scope of practice of a licensed practical nurse.

    (ii) The standards of conduct for members of the nursing profession and, in particular, a licensed practical nurse.

    (iii) Historical perspectives of nursing and current legal-ethical issues.

    (iv) Licensure requirements.

  (d) Select cooperating agencies that meet the requirements of R 338.10307(5), (6), and (8).

) A licensed practical nursing education program may substitute up to 50% of clinical hours in any single course with simulation laboratory experiences, except for pediatric and obstetric clinical hours. A licensed practical nursing education program may substitute up to 100% of pediatric and obstetric clinical hours with simulation laboratory. For simulation laboratory experiences, the board adopts by reference the standards of the International Nursing Association for Clinical Simulation and Learning, as specified in the publication entitled, "Standards of Best Practice: Simulation" 2016. The standards are available from the International Nursing Association for Clinical Simulation and Learning's website at:http://www.inacsl.org at no cost. Copies of the standards are available for inspection and distribution at cost from the Board of Nursing, Bureau of Professional Licensing, Department of Licensing and Regulatory Affairs, 611 W. Ottawa Street, P.O. Box 30670, Lansing, Michigan 48909. R 338.10310 Board evaluation of a nursing education program. (State of Michigan, 2020).

nursing program may fall under **Board review** if any of the following circumstances present:

(a) A request for initiating a program of nursing education is submitted.

(b) A request for full approval of a program is submitted.

(c) A request for approval of a major program change is submitted.

(d) The pass rate for first-time test takers on the required licensure NCLEX examination is less than 80% for any 1 year of compiled statistics provided from the National Council of State Boards of Nursing.

e) Complaints regarding the conduct of the program are received and it is necessary to validate the complaints, pursuant to section 17242 of the code, MCL 333.17242.

(f) Failure of a nursing education program to submit a nursing education program report, or self-study report pursuant to the time frames set forth in R 338.10303b.

(g) Failure of a nursing education program to submit faculty exception requests before the start date of the semester under R 338.10305a and R 338.10305b.

(h) Program completion rate of less than 75% as submitted on a nursing education program report. The rate is calculated by determining the number of students who complete the nursing program in no more than 150% of the stated program length.

(i) Failure of the nursing education program to evaluate a program to apply for full approval by the end of the fourth cohort.

(j) Failure of a nursing education program to submit an annual nursing education program report pursuant to the time frames set forth in R 338.10303(d). (State of Michigan, 2020).

Nursing Educational and Professional Ladders

Nursing Education Programs

The nursing profession has diverse entry points and provides myriad opportunities for the advancement of education and practice. Nursing education programs in Michigan and around the country provide tracks for students to earn Associate, Bachelor, Master, and Doctoral degrees. Many nursing schools offer specific programs that expedite the learning process for students who already have clinical experience and/or other healthcare licensing (e.g. paramedics, respiratory therapists). Accelerated nursing programs also exist for students with Bachelor's or higher degrees in other fields seeking to earn a nursing degree. Further, expedited programs exist for current licensed nurses seeking to advance education (e.g. LPN to RN, RN to BSN, RN to MSN). The list below outlines the general types of degrees available within the nursing profession.

Associate Degree in Nursing (ADN) – requires two years of nursing specific education including, clinical components.

Bachelor of Science in Nursing (BSN) – requires four years of nursing specific education, including clinical components.

Master of Science in Nursing (MSN) – requires one to two years of nursing specific education with a specified focus. Certain specialties require clinical components.

Doctor of Nursing Practice (DNP) – requires two to four years of nursing specific education with a focus and increased emphasis on nursing research to impact practice. Certain specialties require clinical components.

Doctor of Philosophy in Nursing (PhD) – requires three to four years of nursing specific education with a focus on advancing the theoretical foundation of nursing practice, education, and research.

By successfully completing nursing programs, students are then eligible to take the exams that enable them to become a licensed professional and practice within an outlined scope (e.g NCLEX to earn RN or LPN status). The list below outlines the various licensures that define the rungs of the professional nursing ladder.

Professional Nursing Roles

Licensed practical nurse (LPN) – requires approximately one year (two semesters) of nursing specific nursing didactic, clinical, and skills curriculum (typically the first part of a nursing program). Practices under the supervision of an RN with less scope of practice. Common practice environments for LPNs include long term care, rehabilitation centers, and community or public health clinics.

Registered nurse (RN) – requires approximately two years (four semesters) of nursing specific didactic, clinical, and skills curriculum. Students successfully completing ADN or BSN programs are eligible for RN licensing. BSN programs require additional coursework to earn the university level degree and provide more education on leadership and research within the profession of nursing. A nurse in this category may have his/her credentials listed as RN, BSN or RN, MSN, or RN, DNP – with the first initials indicating the license level and the second initials indicating the highest educational level. The RN designation indicates that these nurses have at least an Associate level degree and they can be found practicing in clinical, educational, legal, and governmental roles, among many others.

Advanced Practice Registered Nurse (APRN) – requires one to four years of nursing focused education in a specialty area. APRNs in many clinical practice arenas can diagnose, treat, and prescribe within their scope of practice. More specific information on APRNs can be found later in this resource.

Nurse Licensure Exam

National Council of State Boards of Nursing (NCSBN)

The National Council of State Boards of Nursing (NCSBN) is an independent umbrella organization through which all state boards of nursing collaborate on overlapping issues of concern affecting public health, safety and welfare. Members of NCSBN are also involved with the development and evolution of nursing licensure examinations, which were created in part to ensure that licensed nurses are prepared to provide safe and competent patient care. The Michigan Board of Nursing is a member of NCSBN and contracts with the organization to facilitate nursing licensure examinations for nurse candidates in Michigan.

For more information on NCSBN, visit https://www.ncsbn.org/index.htm

National Council Licensing Examination (NCLEX)

The National Council Licensing Examination (NCLEX) is the standardized exam that every nurse candidate must pass to earn a nursing license. It is designed "as a screening tool used to identify candidates that can demonstrate that their nursing ability is sufficient to be competent in practice" (National Council of State Boards of Nursing, 2021).

Two NCLEX exams exist – one for candidates seeking licensure as a practical nurse (LPN), the NCLEX-PN, and another for candidates seeking licensure as a registered nurse (RN), the NCLEX-RN. Some students choose to complete the NCLEX-PN after fulfilling the required course curriculum and gain experience working as an LPN while completing the remainder of the nursing school requirements. The two exams are independent and passing the NCLEX-PN is not a requirement for registering for the NCLEX-RN. The exams are psychometrically designed, with validated results, which makes it a legally defensible evaluation tool.

NCLEX Specifics

Traditional exams administer the same items and level of difficulty to every individual over the same amount of time. However, this method does not provide an accurate representation of an individual's true ability since those with higher abilities will be required to answer all the easy items and those with lower abilities may guess on harder items (National Council of State Boards of Nursing, 2019). The NCLEX provides a unique method of assessment using Computer Adaptive Testing (CAT). NCSBN, in 1994, was the first organization to implement CAT and indicates that this method was adopted for NCLEX testing to provide the following advantages:

1. Reduces the number of "easy" items that high-ability candidates receive; "easy" items tell little about a high performing candidate's ability

2. Reduces the number of "difficult" items low-ability candidates receive; candidates tend to guess on items that are too difficult which can skew results

3. Reduces item exposure and subsequent security risks

4. Improves precision of measurement of the NCLEX candidate's ability related to nursing and provides a valid and reliable measurement of nursing competence

The use of CAT means that each candidate will have a unique and curated NCLEX experience based on his/her ability and performance from question to question.

Test Structure

During the fall of 2020, in response to the COVID-19 pandemic, NCSBN made several temporary modifications to the NCLEX test structure. With continuous evaluation and data analysis, NCSBN concluded that the modifications retained psychometric strength and live test results were not negatively impacted when compared to historical data. Thus, some of the modifications put into place during the pandemic continue. Below is a summary of the overall test structure of the NCLEX effective October 1, 2020:

- The minimum number of items for both the RN and PN exam: 75, including 15 pre-test items, which are not scored, but serve to provide data for improving the integrity of the NCLEX.

- The maximum number of items for both the RN and PN exam: 145

- The total test time for both the RN and PN exam: five hours

- When a candidate runs out of time, the final ability estimate is computed from all responses on all the items completed on the exam. If it is above the standard, it is a pass; otherwise, the exam will be a fail.

NCLEX Test Questions

The NCLEX test questions are written using the framework of Bloom's Taxonomy for cognitive levels with most questions written at the application level or higher since the profession of nursing requires one to apply knowledge or skills to complex and changing patient situations. The test questions are organized into the following major and sub-categories, with the highest percentage of questions distributed in management of care (20%) and pharmacological therapies (15%).

1. **Safe and Effective Care Environment**
   a. Management of Care
   b. Safety and Infection Control

2. **Health Promotion and Maintenance**

3. **Psychosocial Integrity**

4. **Physiological Integrity**
   a. Basic Care and Comfort
   b. Pharmacological and Parenteral Therapies
   c. Reduction of Risk Potential
   d. Physiological Adaptation

The test questions also weave in the fundamental processes of the nursing profession, summarized by NCSBN (2020) as nursing process, caring, communication & documentation, teaching & learning, and culture & spirituality.

Items on the NCLEX may appear as multiple-choice, multiple response, fill-in-the-blank calculation questions, ordered response, and hot spots (items in which the candidate reads a scenario and highlights key words). All item types may include multimedia, such as charts, tables, graphics, or audio.

NCLEX Scoring

Candidates who have completed the NCLEX will receive a score of either pass or fail, reported out to them by the state board of nursing. Candidates who fail will receive detailed feedback to assist them during the remediation process.

The CAT scoring algorithm estimates the ability of the candidate in relation to the established passing standard. Every time the candidate answers an item, the computer re-estimates the candidate's ability. With each additional answered item, the ability estimate becomes more exact.

The computer uses a statistically generated 95% confidence estimate to determine whether the candidate's ability is above or below the designated passing threshold. According to NCSBN (2020), "after the minimum number of items has been answered, the computer compares the candidate's ability level to the standard required for passing. Candidates clearly above the passing standard pass. Candidates clearly below the passing standard fail. If the candidate's ability level is close enough to the passing standard that it is not clear which side of the passing standard his or her ability falls, the computer continues asking items. As more items are answered, the candidate's ability estimate becomes more precise. After each item, the candidate's ability level is recomputed, using all of the information (answers to all the items asked) available at that point. When it becomes clear on which side of the passing standard the candidate's ability falls, the examination ends."

The passing standard is reevaluated once every three years by the NCSBN Board of Directors to set a standard for the minimum level of ability required for safe and effective entry level nursing practice (National Council of State Boards of Nursing, 2021).

NCLEX Next Generation Project

A new and improved NCLEX is scheduled for roll-out in 2023. The Next Generation NCLEX (NGN) will utilize real-world case studies to reflect the kinds of patient interactions and critical decisions nurses make in a multitude of healthcare settings. The case studies will emphasize "interactions between nurse and patient, the patient's needs and expected outcomes" (National Council of State Boards of Nursing, 2021).

In July 2017, NCSBN began administering a "Special Research Section" to select candidates taking the NCLEX. These additional items are administered after candidates complete the NCLEX and the data collected assists in testing the usability of the newly designed prototype items as part of the NGN research project.

The Next Generation NCLEX will include the following new or extended items:

- **Extended multiple response** – this item will still require the candidate to select all of the correct options and none of the incorrect options, but will have an increased number of options to choose from and allow partial credit scoring.

- **Extended drag & drop** – this item currently requires candidates to arrange all options into a time-sequenced order. The NGN version will look similar to the current drag & drop questions, allowing candidates to move or place response options into answer spaces, but may contain some options that do not apply to the scenario (more options than answer spaces).

- **Cloze (drop down)**– this new item will allow candidates to select one option from a drop down list. There can be more than one drop-down list in a cloze item. The drop-down lists can be words or phrases within a sentence, tables or charts.

- **Extended hot spot (highlighting)** – this item will allow candidates to select the answer by highlighting words or phrases within a portion of a patient's health record that answer the question.

- **Matrix grid** – this new item will allow candidates to select multiple answer options in each row or column. This can be useful in measuring various facets of a clinical scenario.

For more information on The Next Generation NCLEX, visit: https://www.ncsbn.org/next-generation-nclex.htm

Michigan Licensure Requirements for Registered Nurses

The general minimum requirements needed to obtain a registered and/or practical nurse license and specialty certifications include the following sections of application process, fees, requirements (revised 9/2019).

Michigan RN License Application & Fees

The online licensure application can be completed by visiting www.michigan.gov/miplus.

Application Fee: (Must be paid online by Visa, Mastercard, or Discover credit or debit card.):

RN or LPN by Examination $208.80 (Valid for 2 years from date issued)

RN or LPN by Endorsement $208.80 (Valid for 2 years from date issued)

RN Specialty Certification: $40.55 or $55.45 (Valid for up to 1 to 2 year(s) from date issued)

RN or LPN re-licensure: $228.80 (Valid for 2 years from date issued)

The following general application requirements apply to all licensure applicants (EXCEPT RENEWAL)

■ **Criminal Background Check** – Once the online application is completed and submitted you will be emailed an application confirmation letter containing instructions to complete the criminal background check (except those applicants seeking re-licensure, if the license expired within the last three years.)

■ **Good Moral Character Questions** – Documentation will be required if you answer "yes" to either question to show at the current time you can, and are likely to, serve the public in a fair, honest and open manner, that you are rehabilitated, or that the substance of the former offense is not reasonably related to the occupation or profession for which you are seeking a license.

■ **Human Trafficking** – Beginning January 6, 2022, completion of training to identify victims of human trafficking is required for initial licensure.

■ **Social Security Number** – An individual applying for licensure is required to provide his or her Social Security number (SSN) at the time of application. If the applicant is exempt under law from obtaining an SSN or does not have an SSN, the SSN affidavit form will be required to be uploaded at the time the application is submitted.

■ **Verification of Licensure** – If you hold a current license or ever held a license as a nurse, verification of licensure will be required to be submitted directly to the office by the licensing agency of any state in which you hold or ever held a license. Verification can be emailed to bpldata@michigan.gov or mailed to Bureau of Professional Licensing, PO BOX 30670, Lansing, MI 48909

■ **Professional Education** – Name of School Attended and Name of Educational Program(s) (LARA, 2021).

Requirements for Michigan RN licensure by exam for those who are graduates of approved nursing schools in the United States

The general application requirements apply and include the following additional requirements:

- Final, official transcripts or the Michigan Nursing School Certification Form, if applicable. This must be submitted directly to the LARA Bureau of Professional Licensing (BPL) office from the nursing school attended and meet the standards set forth by the Board.
- Passing NCLEX-RN Examination Scores – Score reports will be received directly from the National Council of State Boards of Nursing (NCSBN).

(LARA, 2021)

Requirements for Michigan RN licensure by endorsement for those who are licensed as a registered nurse in another state

The general application requirements apply and include the following additional requirements:

- Must possess an active, unencumbered license in another state and have been initially licensed by NCLEX examination in another state. Verification of licensure must be submitted directly to the office by the licensing agency of any state in which the license is held.
- If an approved Registered Nurse program located in the United States or Canada was not completed, additional certification through the Certification Program of the Commission on Graduates of Foreign Nursing Schools will be required. This must be submitted directly to the LARA Bureau of Professional Licensing (BPL) office from CGFNS and meet the standards set forth by the Board.
- If an applicant is a graduate of a Registered Nurse education program that is located outside of the United States, has passed the NCLEX-RN examination, and has maintained an active license with no disciplinary sanctions in the United States for at least 5 years immediately preceding the application for a Michigan license, then the applicant shall be exempt from completing the nursing education review and the certification process through the certification program (LARA, 2021).

Requirements for Michigan RN licensure by exam for graduates of foreign nursing schools

The general application requirements apply and include the following additional requirements:

- Verification of obtaining certification from the Commission on Graduates of Foreign Nursing Schools (CGFNS) Certification Program. This must be submitted directly to the LARA Bureau of Professional Licensing (BPL) office from CGFNS and meet the standards set forth by the Board.
- An applicant shall be exempt from completing the CGFNS Certification Program if an applicant is a graduate of a Canadian Registered Nurse program that is approved by a province of Canada, the program was taught in English, and the applicant has a current active license to practice nursing in Canada and has not been sanctioned by the applicable Canadian nursing authority. If these requirements are met, verification of licensure must be submitted directly to the office by the Canadian licensing agency in which the license is held.
- Final official transcripts from the approved Canadian school also must be submitted directly to the office from the nursing school attended. Verification of Licensure and transcripts can be emailed to bpldata@ michigan.gov or mailed to Bureau of Professional Licensing, PO BOX 30670, Lansing, MI 48909.

- Passing NCLEX-RN Examination Scores. Score reports will be received directly from the National Council of State Boards of Nursing (NCSBN).
- Professional Education – Name of school attended, and name of educational program completed. (LARA, 2021)

Additional requirements for those who hold current specialty certification for a nurse anesthetist, nurse midwife, nurse practitioner, or clinical nurse specialist

- Holds a current and valid Registered Nurse license in Michigan.
- Possesses national certification from a certification organization that meets the standards set forth by the Board. Verification of current certification as a nurse anesthetist, nurse midwife, nurse practitioner, or clinical nurse specialist must be submitted directly to the office from the certifying agency. (LARA, 2021)

Additional requirements for Michigan LPN license by exam for those who are graduates of approved nursing schools located in the United States

- Final, official transcripts or the Michigan Nursing School Certification Form, if applicable. This must be submitted directly to bpldata@michigan.gov or mailed to Bureau of Professional Licensing, PO BOX 30670, Lansing, MI 48909 from the nursing school attended and meet the standards set forth by the Board.
- Passing NCLEX-LPN examination scores. Score reports will be received directly from the National Council of State Boards of Nursing (NCSBN). (LARA, 2021)

Additional requirements for Michigan LPN licensure by exam for those who are graduates of foreign nursing schools

- Verification of obtaining a professional report evaluation of education completed by the Credentials Evaluation Service (CES) of CGFNS or have a full course-by-course credential evaluation of your education certified by a National Association of Credential Evaluation Services (NACES) member organization. This must be submitted directly to bpldata@michigan.gov or mailed to Bureau of Professional Licensing, PO BOX 30670, Lansing, MI 48909 from CGFNS or NACES agency and meet the standards set forth by the Board.
- An applicant shall be exempt from completing the CGFNS or NACES certification process if an applicant is a graduate of a Canadian Registered Nurse program that is approved by a province of Canada, the program was taught in English, the applicant has a current active license to practice nursing in Canada and has not been sanctioned by the applicable Canadian nursing authority. Verification of licensure must be submitted directly to bpldata@michigan.gov or mailed to Bureau of Professional Licensing, PO BOX 30670, Lansing, MI 48909 by the Canadian licensing agency in which you hold or ever held a license.
- Final Official Transcripts from the approved, Canadian School will also be required to be submitted directly to this office from the nursing school attended. Verification of Licensure and transcripts can be emailed to bpldata@michigan.gov or mailed to Bureau of Professional Licensing, P.O. Box 30670, Lansing, MI 48909.
- Passing NCLEX-LPN examination scores. Score reports will be received directly from the National Council of State Boards of Nursing (LARA, 2021).

Additional requirements for Michigan licensure by endorsement for those licensed as a practical nurse in another state

■ Must possess an active, unencumbered license in another state and have been initially licensed by NCLEX-LPN examination in another state. Verification of licensure must be submitted directly to the office by the licensing agency of any state in which the license is held.

■ If the applicant did not complete an approved, educational program located in the United States or Canada, a professional report evaluation of the education completed by the Credentials Evaluation Service (CES) of CGFNS is required or have a full course-by-course credential evaluation of the education certified by a National Association of Credential Evaluation Services (NACES) member organization. This must be submitted directly to the office from CGFNS or NACES agency and meet the standards set forth by the Board.

■ If an applicant is a graduate of a Licensed Practical Nurse education program that is located outside of the United States, has passed the NCLEX-LPN examination, and has maintained an active license with no disciplinary sanctions in the United States for at least 5 years immediately preceding the application for a Michigan license, then the applicant shall be exempt from completing the nursing educational review and certification process through either CGFNS or NACES (LARA, 2021)

> " "
>
> *The National Council Learning Examination is the standardized exam that every nursing student in the United States must complete in order to become a registered nurse and use the credentials RN after her or his name.*

CONTINUING EDUCATION REQUIREMENTS FOR MICHIGAN NURSES

Authority: Public Act 368 of 1978, as amended.

This section explains the requirements and the license renewal process for every nurse licensed to practice in Michigan.

REQUIREMENTS

- The Michigan Public Health Code and Michigan Board of Nursing administrative rules require every nurse to complete, during the 2-year period prior to the renewal of the license, at least 25 hours of continuing education, with at least two (2) hours in pain and symptom management, in courses or programs approved by the Board. Pursuant to this requirement, the Board has promulgated rules to establish specific criteria for the Board's approval of continuing education courses and programs.

- The continuing education requirements apply to every nurse renewing a Michigan license who held the license for the 2-year period immediately preceding the date of the license renewal. The requirements apply whether or not the nurse is actively engaged in the practice of nursing. No one is exempt from this requirement.

- Each nurse is required to complete not less than 25 hours of continuing education hours that are approved by the Board during the 2 years preceding an application for renewal or re-licensure. Beginning 1-6-2017, at least 2 of these hours must be in pain and symptom management.

- **Pain management education requirement:** continuing education contact hours in pain and pain symptom management may include, but are not limited to, courses in behavior management, psychology of pain, pharmacology, behavior modification, stress management, clinical applications, and drug interventions.

- **Human trafficking education requirement:** added to the Board of Nursing General Rules effective September 23, 2019: individuals licensed or seeking licensure shall complete a one-time training in identifying victims of human trafficking. For full rule details visit https://www.michigan.gov/lara/

- **Implicit bias education requirement:** on June 1, 2021, the Michigan Public Health Code General Rules adopted the addition of code R 338.7004 specifically outlining implicit bias training standards which state that starting in 2022, all applicants for licensure or renewal must complete a minimum of 2 hours of training in implicit bias within the five years immediately preceding registration. For example, an applicant seeking license renewal in 2022 who completed a training related to implicit bias in the years 2018-2022 that meets the specified standards may fulfill this requirement.

- Every nurse who is renewing his/her license should retain records documenting the completion of continuing education. Those documents should be retained for a period of 4 years after the renewal of the license.

- DO NOT SEND THE CONTINUING EDUCATION DOCUMENTS along with the license renewal application. The Department of Licensing and Regulatory Affairs, Bureau of Professional Licensing will conduct an audit at the conclusion of the renewal period. Nurses chosen for audit through an automated random selection process will be contacted by letter to submit documented evidence of the completion of 25 hours of continuing education hours with 2 hours in pain & pain symptom management.

- DO NOT RENEW YOUR LICENSE IF YOU DO NOT HAVE THE REQUIRED 25 HOURS OF CONTINUING EDUCATION CONTACT HOURS.

- A nurse who is unable to provide evidence of completion of the continuing education requirements when requested is in violation of the Michigan Public Health Code and subject to one or more of the following possible license sanctions: reprimand, probation, denial, suspension, revocation, limitation, restitution, and fine.

- If a licensee holds both an RN and LPN license and both licenses expire in the same year, continuing education contact hours earned may be applied to both licenses. However, if a licensee holds an RN and LPN license, and one expires in one year and the other expires in the following year, the contact hours may overlap as long as they are earned within 2 years of the expiration of the license being renewed.

- Accredited sponsors are required to provide attendance certificates that indicate name of licensee, program dates and number of designated hours. Further information about programs with accredited sponsorship may be obtained by contacting the accredited sponsor. "Contact hour" is the same as one 50-60 minute or (1) credit hour (LARA, 2021)

Additional requirements for Michigan RN/LPN re-licensure applicants

"Re-licensure" means the granting of a license to a person whose license has lapsed for failure to renew the license within 60 days after the expiration date.

- Continuing Education – Submit proof of having completed 25 hours of continuing education in courses and programs approved by the board, including at least 2 hours in pain and symptom management, all of which were earned within the 2 year-period immediately preceding the application for re-licensure.

- If the Michigan license has been lapsed for less than 3 years and a current and valid license in another state is held, proof of continuing education is not required.

- Certification of Skill Competency – Submit proof of written certification of skill competency that meets the standards set forth by the Board. If the Michigan license has been lapsed for less than 3 years and/or a current and valid license is held from another state, proof of skills competency is not required.

- Passing NCLEX Examination Scores – If the Michigan license has been lapsed for 7 years or more and a current and valid license in another state is not held, submission of NCLEX exam scores will be required.

- Good Moral Character Questions – Documentation will be required if an applicant answers "yes" to either question to show at the current time that he/she can, and are likely to, serve the public in a fair, honest and open manner, that he/she is rehabilitated, or that the substance of the former offense is not reasonably related to the occupation or profession for which he/she is seeking license renewal.

- Disciplinary Question – Documentation will be required if an applicant answers "yes" to having sanctions imposed by a similar licensure, registration, certification, or disciplinary board of another state or country that has not been previously reported to the department.

- Human Trafficking – Beginning in 2019, and all renewals thereafter, licensees seeking renewal must have completed training in identifying victims of human trafficking that meets the standards in Administrative Rule 338.10105 prior to renewing their license. The training must only be completed one time.

- If a prescriber or dispenser is delegating or ordering the prescribing, dispensing, or administering of a controlled substance to a nurse, the nurse must have completed prior to renewal a 1-time training in opioids and controlled substance awareness that meets the standards established in Administrative Rule 338.3135 (LARA, 2021).

'Accept Renewal' Attestation - By accepting the renewal attestation, the licensee certifies that he/she has met all of the following continuing education requirements during the 2-year period immediately preceding the application for renewal:

- 25 hours of continuing education in courses or programs approved by the Board of which includes a minimum of 2 hours in pain and pain and symptom management.

Additional information regarding continuing education can be found by accessing the Administrative Rules for Nursing at: www.michigan.gov/healthlicense and click on the nursing link.

Administrative Rules for Continuing Education: Relicensure

"Re-licensure" means the granting of a license to a person whose license has lapsed for failure to renew the license within 60 days after the expiration date.

Nurses applying for re-licensure pursuant to R338.10601 – all relicensure applicants must have earned 25 hours approved continuing education contact hours with at least two (2) hours in pain & pain symptom management during the 2-year period prior to the application for relicensure.

Rule 602 (R 338.10602) Acceptable Continuing Education

Rule 2(a): The following accrediting organizations, boards, and programs are permitted by the Michigan Board of Nursing to approve nursing continuing education providers for Michigan. The Board will consider any of the following as providing acceptable continuing education for license renewal or re-licensure without limitation:

- ACCREDITATION COUNCIL FOR CONTINUING MEDICAL EDUCATION
- AMERICAN ASSOCIATION OF NURSE ANESTHETISTS
- AMERICAN COLLEGE OF NURSING MIDWIVES
- AMERICAN ASSOCIATION OF NURSE PRACTITIONERS
- NATIONAL ASSOCIATION OF CLINICAL NURSE SPECIALISTS
- AMERICAN NURSES CREDENTIALING CENTER
- AMERICAN OSTEOPATHIC ASSOCIATION
- ANOTHER STATE OR PROVINCIAL BOARD OF NURSING
- NATIONAL ASSOCIATION FOR PRACTICAL NURSE EDUCATION AND SERVICE INC
- NATIONAL LEAGUE FOR NURSING
- NURSING EDUCATION PROGRAM APPROVED BY THE BOARD

If audited, a licensee shall submit a copy of a letter or certificate of completion showing the applicant's name, number of hours earned, sponsor name or the name of the organization that approved the program or activity for continuing education credit, and the date on which the program was held or activity was completed.

Rule 2(b): A licensee may earn 5 hours of continuing education for each semester credit hour earned for the completion of academic courses related to nursing practice offered in a nursing education program approved by the board. (Three hours of continuing education may be earned for each quarter credit hour earned.)

audited, a licensee shall submit an official transcript that reflects completion of the academic course and umber of semester or quarter credit hours earned.

ule 2(c): A licensee may earn 25 hours of continuing education for obtaining specialty certification or maintaining ertification as a clinical nurse specialist, nurse midwife, nurse anesthetist, or nurse practitioner.

audited, a licensee shall submit proof of certification or recertification.

ule 2(d): A licensee may earn 10 hours of continuing education for successful completion of a national nursing pecialty examination in the year which the licensee achieves a passing score. A maximum of 20 hours may be arned in the renewal period. Credit will not be given for repeating the same examination in a renewal period.

audited, a licensee shall submit proof of a passing score on the examination.

ule 2(e): A licensee may earn 10 hours of continuing education for initial publication of a chapter, or an article elated to the practice of nursing or allied health in either of the following: A nursing or health care textbook; peer- reviewed textbook; a nursing or health care peer-reviewed journal. A maximum of 10 hours may be arned in each renewal period.

audited, the licensee shall submit a copy of the publication that identifies the licensee as the author or a ublication acceptance letter.

ule 2(f): A licensee may earn 1 hour for each 50-60 minutes of participation in independent reading of articles r viewing or listening to media related to nursing practice that do not include a self- assessment component. A aximum of 4 hours may be earned in each renewal period.

audited, the licensee shall submit an affidavit attesting to the number of hours the licensee spent participating these activities and that includes a description of the activity.

ule 2(g): A licensee may earn 1 hour for each 60 minutes of participation on a health care organization ommittee dealing with quality patient care or utilization review. A maximum of 4 hours may be earned in each enewal period.

audited, the licensee shall submit a letter from an organization official verifying the applicant's participation nd the number of hours the applicant spent participating on the committee.

ule 2(h): A licensee may earn 3 hours of continuing education for each 60 minutes of presentation of an cademic or continuing education program that is not a part of the applicant's regular job description. A maximum f 6 hours may be earned in each renewal period.

audited, a licensee shall submit a copy of the curriculum and a letter from the program sponsor verifying the ength and date of the presentation.

ule 2(i): A licensee may earn continuing education for participation as a preceptor for at least 1 nursing tudent or new employee undergoing orientation. A preceptorship shall be for a minimum of 120 hours and have 1 student/employee to 1 preceptor ratio. This may involve more than 1 student or employee. A maximum of 5 ours may be earned in each renewal period.

audited, a licensee shall submit written documentation from the educational institution or preceptor's supervisor erifying the dates and hours of the preceptorship.

Continuing Education Waivers

he Michigan Public Health Code authorizes the Board of Nursing to waive the continuing education requirements r a license renewal applicant if, upon written application, the board finds the failure of the licensee to attend the required board-approved courses or programs was due to the licensee's disability, military service, absence from the continental United States, or a circumstance beyond the control of the licensee which the board considers good and sufficient. Pursuant to this authority, the board has promulgated guidelines that set forth the policy the board will follow in granting a waiver. The guidelines provide for the following:

DISABILITY: The licensee's disability shall have been temporary in nature and the licensee's physician shall attest on the application that the disability no longer prevents the licensee from attending educational programs and engaging in the practice of nursing without limitation.

MILITARY SERVICE: The licensee shall have been practicing nursing while in active service of the United States, shall have been licensed at the time of induction or entering into service, and shall have requested that his or her license be placed in military status to continue in effect without payment of the license renewal fee pursuant to Section 16196 of the Public Health Code.

ABSENCE FROM THE UNITED STATES: The licensee shall establish that board-approved educational programs were not available within a reasonable distance from which the licensee was located and the licensee shall provide evidence of attendance at educational programs that substantially meet the requirements for approval by the board.

OTHER CIRCUMSTANCES BEYOND LICENSEE'S CONTROL: For circumstances, other than disability, military service, or absence from the continental United States, the licensee shall submit compelling evidence that the circumstances were good and sufficient for a waiver of the requirements.

If the board finds that any of the conditions for waiving the requirements have been met, the number of hours waived shall be proportional to the length of time the licensee was temporarily disabled, in active military service, outside the continental United States, or involved in circumstances beyond the licensee's control. The board will not waive the requirements prospectively, nor will the requirements be waived for a licensee whose circumstances changed in time to reasonably allow the licensee to complete all or part of the requirements before license renewal.

Summary of Continuing Education for Licensure

■ All Michigan licensed nurses must complete 25 hours of board approved continuing education, with at least 2 hours in pain and pain symptom management, within the 2 years immediately preceding the expiration date of their license.

■ Submission of the renewal application and fee is considered a statement that the continuing education requirement has been met.

■ Failure to complete the continuing education requirement is considered a violation of the Michigan Public Health Code.

The Department of Licensing and Regulatory Affairs will not discriminate against any individual or group because of race, sex, religion, age, national origin, color, marital status, disability or political beliefs. If you need assistance with reading, writing, hearing, etc., under the Americans with Disabilities Act, you may make your needs known to LARA.

Bias & Inequity in Healthcare

Disparities, linked to a dramatically imbalanced power system, have existed in the United States since its inception; thus, disparities in healthcare seem to be an extension of the inequitable and unjust practices sewn into the fabric of the nation. Despite the historical and well documented patterns of inequity, there has been a slow progression of acknowledgement and attention to eliminating such disparities in healthcare on a large scale.

In 1990, the Centers for Disease Control (CDC) established "reducing disparities among American people" as one of the over-arching goals for the Healthy People 2000 campaign

(CDC, 1993). Although some strides have been made since then to highlight disparities, the efforts in reducing them have focused more on validating the unproven notions that Black people (and other non-white bodies) are inferior and/or more prone to illness/disease (and perhaps eliminating disparities may not be possible). Instead of asking marginalized communities with higher rates of co-morbidities and mortality rates, documented in the data for centuries, "what has happened to you?", healthcare systems and their human mediators, have asked "what did you do or not do?" to become poorer, sicker, or less educated. Therefore, the healthcare system, working from the context of "unsubstantiated assumptions about the biological nature of race has contaminated scientific and medical reasoning in both subtle and profound ways" with disastrous consequences (National Institutes on Minority and Health Disparities, 2021).

In 2020, the COVID-19 pandemic ravaged Black and Brown communities in the United States, shattering the illusion that inequity was something the nation could blame on biology or skin color. Over 30 years after establishing a goal to "reduce disparities", in 2021, the CDC publicly recognized racism as a "public health crisis" and acknowledged that structural racism and implicit bias have played leading roles in the disparities of health care, health education, and access to insurance as well as treatment. The pandemic swiftly evinced in real time what the research across varied disciplines had already documented for years – that the rampant inequity people of color experience within healthcare settings results in part from structural and personal bias and "judgmental care" (American Nurses Association, 2021; Fitzgerald & Hurst, 2017; Institute of Medicine, 2003).

The American Nurses Association (ANA) stresses that the profession of nursing is rooted in the art of caring for the human person, which is a sacred relationship and demands that "nurses know themselves and work on the evolution of nonjudgmental attitudes" (ANA, 2021, p. 23). Patients trust nurses in a unique and unparalleled way and that trust must not be violated by biases that may permeate the layers of the nursing process.

Further, ANA asserts that social justice is a critical component to the work and profession of nursing and involves "analysis, critique, and change of social structures, policies, laws, customs, power and privilege that disadvantage or harm vulnerable social groups through marginalization, exclusion, exploitation, and voicelessness" (ANA, 2021, p. 23). If nursing is the last layer of defense between the patient and harm, then it should include protection from the nurse as well (ANA, 2021).

In the state of Michigan, specifically, the COVID-19 pandemic has highlighted the extreme disparities in health care access, delivery, and outcomes across racial lines. In the first 6 months of the pandemic, over three times as many Black people died from COVID-19 as compared to whites and Black nurses were more likely than white nurses to care for COVID-19 patients or contract the disease (Michigan Department of Health & Human Services, 2020).

Based on the overwhelming data and recommendations from the COVID-19 Task Force on Racial Disparities commissioned by Governor Whitmer in 2020, an educational mandate for all licensed healthcare providers to receive comprehensive implicit bias training as a licensing requirement was established.

The Michigan Department of Licensing & Regulatory Affairs (LARA) filed the final rules for implicit bias training for healthcare providers which included revisions to several amendments within the Michigan Public Health Code General Rules and the addition of code R 338.7004 specifically outlining implicit bias training standards. The rules were adopted on June 1, 2021.

The full rules and details taken directly from the Michigan Public Health Code are outlined below. To summarize the basic requirements: beginning in June 2022, all nurses seeking licensure in Michigan must complete a minimum of 2 hours of training in implicit bias within the five years immediately preceding registration. For every renewal cycle thereafter, all nurses seeking re-licensure must complete a minimum of 2 hours of training in implicit bias. Details regarding the requirements of the training as follows:

Administrative rules: Implicit bias training standards (R 338.7004)

Rule 4.

(1) Beginning 1 year after promulgation of this rule, an applicant for licensure or registration under article 15 of the code, MCL 333.16101 to 333.18838, except those seeking to be licensed under part 188 of the code, MCL 333.18801 to 333.18838, shall have completed a minimum of 2 hours of implicit bias training within the 5 years immediately preceding issuance of the license or registration.

(2) Beginning 1 year after promulgation of this rule and for every renewal cycle thereafter, in addition to completing any continuing education required for renewal, an applicant for license or registration renewal under article 15 of the code, MCL 333.16101 to 333.18838, except those licensed under part 188 of the code, MCL 333.18801 to 333.18838, shall have completed a minimum of 1 hour of implicit bias training for each year of the applicant's license or registration cycle.

(3) The implicit bias training must be related to reducing barriers and disparities in access to and delivery of health care services and meet all of the following requirements:

   (a) Training content must include, but is not limited to, 1 or more of the following topics:

   (i) Information on implicit bias, equitable access to health care, serving a diverse population, diversity and inclusion initiatives, and cultural sensitivity.

   (ii) Strategies to remedy the negative impact of implicit bias by recognizing and understanding how it impacts perception, judgment, and actions that may result in inequitable decision making, failure to effectively communicate, and result in barriers and disparities in the access to and delivery of health care services.

   (iii) The historical basis and present consequences of implicit biases based on an individual's characteristics.

   (iv) Discussion of current research on implicit bias in the access to and delivery of health care services.

(b) Training must include strategies to reduce disparities in access to and delivery of health care services and the administration of pre- and post-test implicit bias assessments.

(c) Acceptable sponsors of this training include any of the following:

  (i) Training offered by a nationally-recognized or state-recognized health-related organization.

  (ii) Training offered by, or in conjunction with, a state or federal agency.

  (iii) Training obtained in an educational program that has been approved by any board created under article 15 of the code, MCL 333.16101 to 333.18838, except under part 188 of the code, MCL 333.18801 to 333.18838, for initial licensure or registration or for the accumulation of continuing education credits.

  (iv) Training offered by an accredited college or university.

  (v) An organization specializing in diversity, equity, and inclusion issues.

(d) Acceptable modalities of training include any of the following:

  (i) A teleconference or webinar that permits live synchronous interaction.

  (ii) A live presentation.

  (iii) Interactive online instruction.

) Submission of an application for licensure, registration, or renewal constitutes an applicant's certificate of compliance with the requirements of this rule. A licensee or registrant shall retain documentation of meeting the requirements of this rule for a period of 6 years from the date of applying for licensure, registration, or renewal. The department may select and audit a sample of a licensees or registrants and request documentation of proof of compliance with this rule. If audited by the department, a licensee or registrant shall provide the proof of completion of training, including either of the following:

(a) A completion certificate issued by the training program that includes the date of the training, the program sponsor's name, the title of the program, and licensee's or registrant's name.

(b) A self-attestation by the licensee or registrant that includes the date of the training, the program sponsor's name, the title of the program, and licensee's or registrant's name.

3ias: Associated Terms and Acronyms

ccessibility: ensuring that people with varied levels of physical or cognitive abilities have equal opportunity, ccess, use, and/or entrance to technology, learning and resources.

geism: prejudice or discrimination based on a person's age.

ias: tendency, trend, inclination, feeling, or opinion, especially one that is preconceived or unreasoned

isgender: used to describe people whose gender identity matches their sex assigned at birth.

onfirmation bias: the tendency to seek out information that validates what one already believes

ultural Humility: requires less emphasis on knowledge and competency of different cultures, but instead laces a greater emphasis on a life-long commitment to learning from differences. Cultural humility encourages elf-evaluation and requires an attitude of openness toward others with varying cultures, religions, languages, tuals and expressions of individuality.

Disparities: significant differences or dissimilarities.

Health disparities: a particular type of health difference that is closely linked with social, economic, and/or environmental disadvantage. Health disparities adversely affect groups of people who have systematically experienced greater obstacles to health based on their racial or ethnic group; religion; socioeconomic status; gender; age; mental health; cognitive, sensory, or physical disability; sexual orientation or gender identity; geographic location; or other characteristics historically linked to discrimination or exclusion (USDHHS,2010).

Equality: providing everyone with the same amount of resources; each person receives an equal share regardless of need.

Equity: resources are shared according to each person's needs; meeting people where they are at.

> *Health equity:* attainment of the highest level of health for all people. Achieving health equity requires valuing everyone equally with focused and ongoing societal efforts to address avoidable inequalities, historical and contemporary injustices, and the elimination of health and health care disparities (USDHHS, 2020).

Ethnicity: a cultural pattern shared by people with the same heritage, often times from the same region of the world, which can include but is not limited to language, preferred diet, specific customs or traditions, family roles and religious beliefs.

Ethnocentrism: believing one's culture, belief, or values are superior to another's or that other cultures/beliefs are wrong.

Explicit bias: conscious state in which an individual openly acknowledges and participates in biased statements and viewpoints; the individual holds the belief that their biased views are correct and acts on those beliefs with purpose.

Gender non-conforming: someone who does not subscribe to prevailing cultural and social expectations about what is appropriate gender expression for their perceived gender.

Implicit bias: rooted in the need for the human brain to create cognitive short-cuts to create efficiency in decision-making, it is an unconscious form of bias that influences perception, memory and behavior, which may have negative effects on understanding and actions during human interactions. Implicit biases are changeable.

Inequity: lack of fairness or justice.

Non-binary: people whose gender identity falls outside of the gender binary (i.e. either male/man or female/woman); used to describe experiences that fall outside of the traditional binary gender model.

Prejudice: preconceived opinion that is not based on reason or experience; dislike, hostility, or unjust behavior deriving from preconceived and unfounded opinions.

Race: a concept without a generally agreed upon definition; often used to define people by commonly shared physical traits; human/social construct used to justify unequal treatment of certain groups of people.

Racism: racial prejudice plus power. Defined by the Centers for Disease Control in 2021 as: consisting of structures, policies, practices, and norms—that assigns value and determines opportunity based on the way people look or the color of their skin. This results in conditions that unfairly advantage some and disadvantage others throughout society.

Social determinants of health: the circumstances in which people are born, grow up, live, work and age, and the systems put in place to deal with illness. These circumstances are in turn shaped by a wider set of forces: economics, social policies, and politics (WHO, 2013).

Stereotype: an assumption that all people of the same ethnic or cultural group behave/believe the same way.

Straight/heterosexual: used to describe people who are romantically and sexually attracted to the opposite sex.

BIPOC: Black, Indigenous, Person of Color (use this when talking about more than one group; say "Black" for example, if talking about one person)

POC: People/person of color

AA-PI: Asian American Pacific Islander (Polynesia, Micronesia, Samoa, Fiji, the Maori in New Zealand)

LGBTQIA (may be represented without the IA as LGBTQ+):

Lesbian (women attracted to other women)

Gay (men attracted to other men)

Bisexual (attracted to two or more genders)

Transgender (someone whose gender identity or expression does not conform to what is expected based on the sex they were assigned at birth)

Questioning (unsure of sexual orientation or gender identity)

Intersex (have biological traits that do not match what is typically identified as male or female. There are many different intersex variations. Being intersex is a naturally occurring variation in humans; it is not pathological. Being intersex is not linked to sexual orientation or gender identity).

Asexual or **Ally** (**asexual:** individuals who do not experience, or experience a low level of, sexual desire regardless of romantic involvement, sexual orientation, or gender identification. **ally:** People who identify as cisgender and straight and believe in social and legal equality for LGBTQ+).

The Future of Nursing 2020-2030: Charting a Path to Achieve Health Equity

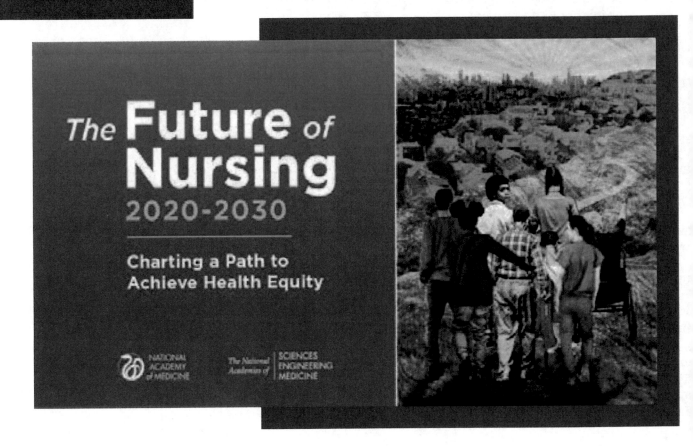

Recommendations at a Glance

Much like Healthy People 2020, The National Academy of Medicine (NAM) has published a blueprint that will explore the future for the next decade of nursing as outlined in the consensus report titled *Future of Nursing 2020-2030: Charting a Path to Achieve Health Equity*, released in May 2021. The work addresses the roots of racial inequity and strategies nurses can employ to improve health outcomes, lifting barriers to expand nurses' scope of practice, addressing nurses' well-being, and diversifying the nursing workforces to address health equity.

#1 *Recommendation: Creating a Shared Agenda*

In 2021, all national nursing organizations should initiate work to develop a shared agenda for addressing social determinants of health and achieving health equity.

Points include:

- ■ Within nursing organizations: Assess & eliminate racist & discriminatory policies.
- ■ External to nursing organizations: Increase the number and diversity of nurses.

#2 Recommendation: Supporting Nurses to Advance Health Equity

y 2023, state and federal government agencies, health care and public health organizations, payers, and undations should initiate substantive actions to enable the nursing workforce to address social determinants health and health equity more comprehensively, regardless of practice setting.

oints include:

- Rapidly increase number of nurses with expertise in health equity and in specialty areas with current shortages.
- Invest in nursing education and traineeships in public health.
- Direct funds to nurses and nursing schools to sustain and increase diversity.

#3 Recommendation: Promoting Nurses' Health and Well-Being

y 2021, nursing education programs, employers, nursing leaders, licensing boards, and nursing organizations hould initiate the implementation of structures, systems, and evidence-based interventions to promote nurses' ealth and well-being, especially as they take on new roles to advance health equity.

oints include:

- Nursing education programs: Integrate content on nurses' health and well-being into their programs.
- Employers: Provide sufficient human and material resources to enable nurses to provide high-quality care effectively and safely.
- Employers: Establish a culture of physical and psychological safety

#4 Recommendation: Capitalizing on Nurses' Potential

ll organizations, including state and federal entities and employing organizations, should enable nurses to ractice to the full extent of their education and training by removing barriers that prevent them from more lly addressing social needs and social determinants of health and improving health care access, quality, and alue. These barriers include regulatory and public and private payment limitations; restrictive policies and actices; and other legal, professional, and commercial impediments.

oints include:

- Changes to institutional policies and laws adopted in response to the COVID-19 pandemic should be made permanent.
- Federal authority (e.g., Veterans Health Administration regulations, Centers for Medicare & Medicaid Services [CMS]) should be used where available to supersede restrictive state laws, including those addressing scope of practice, telehealth, and insurance coverage and payment, that decrease access to care and burden nursing practice, and to encourage nationwide adoption of the Nurse Licensure Compact.

#5 Recommendation: Paying for Nursing Care

ederal, tribal, state, local, and private payers and public health agencies should establish sustainable and exible payment mechanisms to support nurses in both health care and public health, including school nurses, addressing social needs, social determinants of health, and health equity.

Points include:

- Reform fee-for-service payment models.
- Create a National Nurse Identifier.
- Ensure adequate funding for public health nursing.

#6 Recommendation: Using Technology to Integrate Data on Social Determinants of Health (SDOH) into Nursing Practice

All public and private health care systems should incorporate nursing expertise in designing, generating, analyzing and applying data to support initiatives focused on social determinants of health and health equity using diverse digital platforms, artificial intelligence, and other innovative technologies.

Points include:

- Integrate data on SDOH and build a nationwide infrastructure.
- Ensure that health equity data collaboratives improve visualization of data on SDOH
- Provide resources to facilitate telehealth by nurses.

#7 Recommendation: Strengthening Nursing Education

Nursing education programs, including continuing education, and accreditors and the National Council of State Boards of Nursing should ensure that nurses are prepared to address social determinants of health and achieve health equity.

Points include:

- To promote equity, inclusivity, and diversity grounded in social justice, identify and eliminate policies, procedures, curricular content, and clinical experiences that perpetuate structural racism, cultural racism, and discrimination among faculty, staff, and students.
- Increase academic progression for geographically and socioeconomically disadvantaged students through academic partnerships that include community and tribal colleges located in rural and urban underserved areas.
- Ensure that students have learning opportunities with care coordination experiences that include working with health care teams to address individual and family social needs, as well as learning opportunities with multisector stakeholders that include a focus on health in all policies and SDOH. Learning experiences should include working with under- served populations in such settings as federally qualified health centers (FQHCs), rural health clinics, and IHS designated sites.

#8 Recommendation: Preparing Nurses to Respond to Disasters and Public Health Emergencies

To enable nurses to address inequities within communities, federal agencies and other key stakeholders within and outside the nursing profession should strengthen and protect the nursing workforce during the response to such public health emergencies as the COVID-19 pandemic and natural disasters, including those related to climate change.

oints include:

- Develop and support emergency preparedness and response knowledge base of the nursing workforce.
- Lead transformational change in nursing education to address workforce development in disaster nursing and public health preparedness.
- Employer emergency response plans.

9 Recommendation: Building the Evidence Base

ne National Institutes of Health, the Centers for Medicare & Medicaid Services, the Centers for Disease Control nd Prevention, the Health Resources and Services Administration, the Agency for Healthcare Research and uality, the Administration for Children and Families, the Administration for Community Living, and private ssociations and foundations should convene representatives from nursing, public health, and health care to evelop and support a research agenda and evidence base describing the impact of nursing interventions, cluding multisector collaboration, on social determinants of health, environmental health, health equity, and urses' health and well-being.

oints include:

- Develop mechanisms for proposing, evaluating, and scaling evidence-based practice models that leverage collaboration.
- Use evidence-based approaches to increase number and diversity of students from disadvantaged groups.
- Determine evidence-based education strategies for preparing nurses to eliminate structural racism and implicit bias to strengthen culturally competent care.

ource: National Academies of Sciences, Engineering, and Medicine. 2021. The Future of Nursing 2020-2030: harting a Path to Achieve Health Equity. Washington, DC: The National Academies Press. ttps://doi.org/10.17226/25982.

Advanced Practice Registered Nurses (APRNs)

Advance Practice Registered Nurses (APRNs) are registered nurses with advanced education and certification. Given the ongoing shortage of primary care physicians, allowing non-physician professionals, such as APRNs, to practice to the full extent of their education and training gives patients more options and access to more types of services.

APRNs include nurse practitioners, clinical nurse specialists, nurse anesthetists, and nurse midwives. Sometimes called 'midlevel' care providers, APRNs are often primary care providers and are at the forefront of providing preventive care services to the public.

APRNs treat and diagnose illnesses, advise the public on health issues, manage chronic disease, and engage in continuous education to remain ahead of any technological, methodological, or other developments in the field. APRNs hold at least a master's degree, and more frequently doctoral level education in addition to the initial nursing education and licensing required for all Registered Nurses (RNs) (American Nurses Association [ANA], 2021). As licensed, independent practitioners, nurse practitioners (NPs) practice both autonomously and in coordination with health care professionals and other individuals. APRNS are credentialed for clinical practice competency through national board certification for their specialty roles. (American Association for Nurse Practitioners [AANP], 2021)

APRN Practice:
Specialty Role Descriptions

- ■ Nurse Practitioners (NPs) provide primary, acute, and specialty health care across the lifespan through assessment, diagnosis, and treatment of illnesses and injuries.
- ■ Certified Nurse-Midwives (CNMs) provide primary, gynecological, and reproductive health care.
- ■ Clinical Nurse Specialists (CNS) provide diagnosis, treatment, and ongoing management of patients; provide expertise and support to nurses caring for patients; help drive practice changes throughout the organization; and ensure use of best practices and evidence-based care to achieve the best possible patient outcomes.
- ■ Certified Registered Nurse Anesthetists (CRNAs) provide a full range of anesthesia and pain management services (American Nurses Association, 2021).

APRNs in Michigan have guidance for their licensure and practice as RNs do. This guidance includes law and regulation as well as licensure requirements that must be fulfilled in order to provide care and maintain an active license.

The APRN Scope of Practice

Consistent with all registered nurses, APRNs are expected to practice consistent with an ethical code of conduct, national certification, evidence-based principles, and current practice standards, and within the parameters set by their state board of nursing.

- **Who:** Registered Nurses (RN) and Advanced Practice Registered Nurses (APRN) comprise the "who" constituency and have been educated, titled, and maintain active licensure to practice nursing.
- **What:** Nursing is the protection, promotion, and optimization of health and abilities; prevention of illness and injury; facilitation of healing; alleviation of suffering through the diagnosis and treatment of human response; and advocacy in the care of individuals, families, groups, communities, and populations.
- **Where:** Wherever there is a patient in need of care.
- **When:** Whenever there is a need for nursing knowledge, compassion, and expertise.
- **Why:** The profession exists to achieve the most positive patient outcomes in keeping with nursing's social contract and obligation to society (AANP, 2021; ANA, 2021).

APRNs as defined by the law

APRN practice is typically defined nationally by the Nurse Practice Act and governed by states' Boards of nursing, but other laws and regulations may impact practice. In some states nurse-midwives are regulated by a board of Midwifery or public health. In addition, in some states, the CNS category is not identified in the Nurse Practice Act, which means the CNS is held to the same scope of practice as any registered nurse within the state. The scope of practice for CRNAs is fairly standard but is not evident in statute in all states. The Michigan APRN's practice is defined in part by statute as seen in the following section.

The Board of Nursing's Administrative Rules states (R 338.10403) that only nurses certified in a nursing specialty field may hold themselves out to the public as nurse specialist using the title nurse anesthetist, nurse midwife or nurse practitioner. Conduct contrary to this rule is deemed a violation of section 16221(g) of the act.

The Public Health Code (333.16109) states that "Specialty certification" means an authorization to use a title by a licensee who has met qualifications established by a board for registration in a health profession specialty field.

The Public Health Code (333.16105) states that "Health Profession specialty field" means an area of practice established under this article that is within the scope of activities, functions and duties of a licensed health profession and that requires advanced education and training beyond that required for initial licensure (Michigan Legislature, 2021; Mich. Admin. Code R. 338.10404, 2017; Nursing Licensure, 2021).

APRNs and Regulation by the Michigan Public Health Code

The Michigan Public Health Code Act 368 of 1978 serves to regulate some of the practice areas that APRNs practice within, as seen in the following definition:

Section 333.17201 Definitions; principles of construction for APRNs: Sec. 17201.

As used in this part:

(a) "Advanced practice registered nurse" or "a.p.r.n." means a registered professional nurse who has been granted a specialty certification under section 17210 in 1 of the following health profession specialty fields:
(i) Nurse midwifery.

(ii) Nurse practitioner.

(iii) Clinical nurse specialist.

(b) "Physician" means a physician who is licensed under part 170 or part 175.

(c) "Practice of nursing" means the systematic application of substantial specialized knowledge and skill, derived from the biological, physical, and behavioral sciences, to the care, treatment, counsel, and health teaching of individuals who are experiencing changes in the normal health processes or who require assistance in the maintenance of health and the prevention or management of illness, injury, or disability.

(Michigan Legislature, 2021; Mich. Admin. Code R. 338.10404, 2017; Nursing Licensure, 2021).

APRN Independence in Michigan: Supervision

Nursing practice as defined by MI law is not dependent upon physician delegation or supervision, and it is not a subset of medical practice. Nursing is an independent profession. Delegation or supervision does not apply for those acts performed within the nurse's scope of practice.

However, anything beyond the statutorily defined scope of practice for nurses must be performed under the supervision of a licensed physician in Michigan. Those elements of an APRN's practice that fall within their definition/scope and for which the APRN is prepared educationally and experientially constitute the practice of nursing. They do not need supervision.

Supervision is statutorily defined in Michigan Compiled Law (333.16109(2)) as the overseeing of or participation in the work of another individual by a health professional licensed under this article in circumstances where at least all of the following conditions exist:

■ The continuous availability of direct communication in person or by radio, telephone, or telecommunication between the supervised individual and a licensed health professional.

■ The availability of a licensed health professional on a regularly scheduled basis to review the practice of the supervised individual, to provide consultation to the supervised individual, to review records, and to further education the supervised individual in the performance of the individual's functions.

■ The provision by the licensed supervising health professional of predetermined procedures and drug protocol.

APRN Independence in Michigan: Prescribing Authority

The Michigan Public Health Code Act 368 of 1978 (Section 333.17211a) delineates the APRN's authority to prescribe nonscheduled prescription drug or controlled substances with the following:

Section 17211a:

(1) An advanced practice registered nurse may prescribe any of the following:

(a) A nonscheduled prescription drug.

(b) Subject to subsection (2), a controlled substance included in schedules 2 to 5 of part 72, as a delegated act of a physician.

(2) If an advanced practice registered nurse prescribes a controlled substance under subsection (1)(b), both the advanced practice registered nurse's name and the physician's name shall be used, recorded, or otherwise indicated in connection with that prescription. If an advanced practice registered nurse prescribes a controlled substance under subsection (1)(b), both the advanced practice registered nurse's and the

physician's DEA registration numbers shall be used, recorded, or otherwise indicated in connection with that prescription.

) The amendatory act that added this section does not require new or additional third-party reimbursement or mandated worker's compensation benefits for services rendered by an advanced practice registered nurse who is authorized to prescribe nonscheduled prescription drugs and controlled substances included in schedules 2 to 5 of part 72 under this section (Michigan Legislature, 2021; Mich. Admin. Code R. 338.10404: Act 368)

APRN Independence in Michigan: Rounding

Michigan, APRNs may make house calls and healthcare visits independently of a physician as prescribed in ection 333.17214 ('advanced practice registered nurse; calls or rounds') which states that an advanced practice gistered nurse may make calls or go on rounds in private homes, public institutions, emergency vehicles, nbulatory care clinics, hospitals, intermediate or extended care facilities, health maintenance organizations, ursing homes, or other health care facilities. Notwithstanding any law or rule to the contrary, an advanced actice registered nurse may make calls or go on rounds as provided in this section without restrictions on e time or frequency of visits by a physician or the advanced practice registered nurse (Michigan Legislature,)21; Mich. Admin. Code R. 338.10404: Act 368)

APRN Licensure and Certification Requirements in Michigan

lichigan's APRNS are licensed as RNs and receive specialty certification from the Michigan Department of censing and Regulatory Affairs (LARA).

lichigan APRNs can be state-certified based on training and examination in any of four advanced nursing roles: urse midwife, nurse anesthetist, nurse practitioner, or clinical nurse specialist. The state does not distinguish etween nurse practitioners and clinical nurse specialists; both are certified as nurse practitioners (AANP, 2021; urse Licensure, 2021).

tate certification is based on achievement of national certification standards. Other assessments of qualification, uch as criminal background checks and screenings of out-of-state credentials, are carried out when the nurse pplies for an RN license. A nurse who is not licensed as an RN in Michigan will need to apply to the Michigan oard of Nursing. Michigan licenses out-of-state nurses by application for endorsement. The Michigan Board f Nursing is under the banner of the Department of Licensing and Regulatory Affairs (LARA) ttp://www.michigan.gov/lara/0,4601,7-154-72600_72603_27529_27542—,00.html) (LARA, 2021).

APRN Education and Certification Requirements

lichigan Public Health Code dictates that specialty certification be dependent on "advanced education". ducational requirements for advanced practice roles are those set by third party certification agencies.

ccording to Michigan administrative code, standards set by the following organizations are adopted by eference:

- American College of Nurse Midwives Certification Council http://www.amcbmidwife.org/
- American Nurses Credentialing Center http://www.nursecredentialing.org/
- National Certification Board of Pediatric Nurse Practitioners and Nurses http://www.pncb.org/ptistore/control/index
- American Academy of Nurse Practitioners http://www.aanpcert.org/
- National Certification Corporation for Obstetric, Gynecologic, and Neonatal Nursing Specialties http://www.nccwebsite.org/

■ Oncology Nursing Certification Corporation http://www.oncc.org/

National certifying agencies screen academic qualifications before approving candidates for examination. APRNs will provide documents such as transcripts to their certification agency and may also need to verify clinical practicum or specialized experience.

The current Michigan application form lists several approved American Nurses Credentialing Center (ANCC) certifications, some designed for clinical nurse specialists, others for nurse practitioners.

The following NP certifications are accepted:

■ Adult

■ Family

■ Gerontological

■ Pediatric

■ Adult Acute Care

■ Adult Psychiatric and Mental Health

■ Diabetes Management, Advanced

The following CNS certifications can be accepted:

■ Adult Health

■ Pediatric Nursing

■ Gerontological Nursing

■ Public/ Community Health Nursing

■ Adult Psychiatric and Mental Health Nursing

■ Child/ Adolescent Psychiatric and Mental Health Nursing

(Michigan Legislature, 2021; Mich. Admin. Code R. 338.10404; Nursing Licensure, 2021).

Michigan Administrative Rules for Specialty Certification of APRNs

Nurse Practitioners (NPs): Section R. 338.10404b - Specialty certification qualifications; nurse practitioner, Rule 404b. A specialty certification for nurse practitioner shall be granted to a registered professional nurse who satisfies all of the following requirements:

(a) Holds a current and valid license to practice nursing in this state.

(b) Submits an application for certification as a nurse practitioner, on a form provided by the department with the required fee.

(c) Possesses advanced practice certification from 1 of the following certification organizations, or successor organizations:

 (i) The American Nurses Credentialing Center.

 (ii) The Pediatric Nursing Certification Board.

 (iii) The National Certification Corporation for Women's Health Care Nurse Practitioner and Neonatal Nurse Practitioner.

 (iv) The American Academy of Nurse Practitioners for Adult Nurse Practitioners, Family Nurse Practitioners, and Adult-Gerontology Primary Care Nurse Practitioners.

 (v) The Oncology Nursing Certification Corporation.

 (vi) The American Association of Critical Care Nurses Certification Corporation for Acute Care Nurse Practitioner (Mich. Admin. Code R. 338.10404b; 2017 MR 1, Eff. Jan. 6, 2017)

Certified Nurse-Midwives (CNMs): Section R. 338.10404a - Specialty certification qualifications; nurse midwife: Rule 404a. A specialty certification for nurse midwife shall be granted to a registered professional nurse who satisfies all of the following requirements:

(a) Holds a current and valid license to practice nursing in this state.

(b) Submits an application for certification as a nurse midwife on a form provided by the department with the required fee.

(c) Possesses a current certification from the American Midwifery Certification Board, Inc. (AMBC), or a successor organization (Mich. Admin. Code R. 338.10404a; 2017 MR 1, Eff. Jan. 6, 2017)

linical Nurse Specialists (CNS): Section R. 338.10404c - Specialty certification qualifications; clinical nurse **ecialist**, Rule 404c; A specialty certification for a clinical nurse specialist must be granted to a registered **ofessional** nurse who satisfies all of the following requirements:

(a) Holds a current and valid license to practice nursing in this state.

(b) Submits an application for certification as a clinical nurse specialist, on a form provided by the department with the required fee.

(c) Possesses either of the following:

(i) An advanced practice certification from either of the following certification organizations, or successor organizations:

(A) The American Nurses Credentialing Center.

(B) The American Association of Critical Care Nurses Certification Corporation.

(ii) If an applicant is unable to take a national certification exam due to graduation from an accredited clinical nurse specialist masters or doctoral nursing program before the development of clinical nurse specialist core competencies and the requirement of 500 clinical practice hours, he or she may be granted a specialty certification as a clinical nurse specialist based upon submission of a portfolio of evidence that demonstrates knowledge and skill competence in the clinical nurse specialist role and population focus. The portfolio must include all of the following:

(A) Transcripts from an accredited masters or doctoral level educational program in clinical nursing with preparation as a clinical nurse specialist.

(B) Curriculum vitae demonstrating work history in a clinical nurse specialist position before April 9, 2017.

(C) Three letters of recommendation, including 1 from a clinical nurse specialist with national board certification and 2 letters from nursing administrators, nursing supervisors, or advanced practice nurses attesting that the applicant has at least 3,000 hours of practice as a clinical nurse specialist before April 9, 2017. These letters must provide evidence that the applicant engaged in practice consistent with the standards for a clinical nurse specialist as described by the National Association of Clinical Nurse Specialists (NACNS) in the publication entitled "Clinical Nurse Specialist and Core Competencies" 2010, which is adopted by reference. A copy of the standards and requirements is available at no cost from the association's website atwww.nacns.org. A copy of the standards and requirements also is available for inspection and distribution at no cost from the Board of Nursing, Michigan Department of Licensing and Regulatory Affairs, 611 West Ottawa, Lansing, MI 48909

oplication for certification as a clinical nurse specialist granted under the criteria set forth in subrule (1)(c)(ii) this rule is not permitted after March 8, 2020 (Mich. Admin. Code R. 338.10404c, 2018 AACS; 2020 MR 7, **ff.** April 6, 2020)

ertified Registered Nurse Anesthetists (CRNAs): Section R. 338.10404 - Specialty certification **ualifications;** nurse anesthetist: Rule 404. A specialty certification for a nurse anesthetist shall be granted to a **gistered** professional nurse who satisfies all of the following requirements:

(a) Holds a current and valid license to practice nursing in this state.

(b) Submits an application for certification as a nurse anesthetist on a form provided by the department, with the required fee.

(c) Possesses current certification from the National Board on Certification and Recertification of Nurse Anesthetists (NBCRNA), or a successor organization

(Michigan Legislature, 2021; Mich. Admin. Code R. 338.10404).

APRN Application Process for Licensure

Michigan does not issue temporary permits to advanced practice nurses; they will be expected to meet all requirements before credentialing.

Applications are available for download from the Licensing and Regulatory Affairs (LARA) website.

APRN License Renewal Requirements

The Michigan specialty credential is normally renewed every two years. The first renewal period, however, may be shorter.

Continuing education standards for advanced practice are, in most cases, set by the certifying agency. The specialty nurse will verify continuing certification and will need to meet a separate set of requirements to renew his or her RN license. Standards may also be set or endorsed by the APRN state-level specialty nursing organization. Michigan has multiple specialty nursing organizations, including the following:

- Michigan Council of Nurse Practitioners http://micnp.org/
- Michigan Association of Clinical Nurse Specialists https://micns.nursingnetwork.com/
- Michigan Association of Nurse Anesthetists http://www.miana.org/
- Michigan Affiliate of the American College of Nurse-Midwives http://michigan.midwife.org/

Each APRN practice specialty has individual licensure renewal requirements as outlined in the Michigan Administrative Rules by section. Further detail can be found at the following sites:

- Section R. 338.10405 - Nurse anesthetist specialty certification renewal or reregistration; schedule; requirements; maintenance of evidence of compliance
- Section R. 338.10405a - Nurse midwife specialty certification renewal or reregistration; schedule; requirements; maintenance of evidence of compliance
- Section R. 338.10405b - Nurse practitioner specialty certification renewal or reregistration; schedule; requirements; maintenance of evidence of compliance
- Section R. 338.10405c - Clinical nurse specialist specialty certification renewal; schedule; requirements; maintenance of evidence of compliance
- Section R. 338.10406 - Expired certification (Michigan Legislature, 2021)

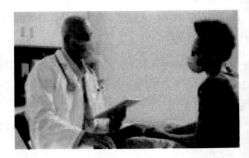

Delegation in Nursing Practice

ealth care is continuously changing and necessitates adjustment for evolving roles and responsibilities of licensed health care providers and assistive personnel. The abilities to delegate, assign and supervise are critical competencies for every RN. Delegation for RNs is a complex process in which the authority to perform a selected nursing task is transferred to a competent licensed or unlicensed individual (or unlicensed assistive personnel) (UAP) in a specific situation. It is important to note that states/jurisdictions have different laws and rules/regulations about delegation, and it is the responsibility of all licensed nurses to know what is permitted in their state. When certain nursing care needs to be delegated, it is imperative that the delegation process and the state Nurse Practice Act (NPA) be clearly understood so that it is safely, ethically and effectively carried out. In Michigan, nurses do not follow a Nurse Practice Act (NPA) and should instead follow both the national standards and the Michigan State Board of Nursing Rules.

The delegation process is multifaceted. It begins with the administrative level of the organization including determining nursing responsibilities that can be delegated, to whom, and what circumstances; developing delegation policies and procedures; periodically evaluating delegation processes; promoting positive culture/ work environment. Then the licensed nurse must be responsible for determining patient needs and when to delegate, ensure availability to delegate, evaluate outcomes of and maintain accountability for delegated responsibility. Finally, the delegatee must accept activities based on their competency level, maintain competence for delegated responsibility and maintain accountability for delegated activity.

The decision to delegate and the supervision of delegation of nursing tasks rest solely with the registered nurse, who makes the determination to delegate based on nursing assessment and in compliance with applicable laws and guidance provided by professional nursing associations (American Nurses Association [ANA]/National Council of State Boards of Nursing [NCSBN], 2006; NASN, 2010).

The registered nurse (registered nurse currently licensed by the Michigan Board of Nursing and working in a healthcare setting) is the coordinator/facilitator of health care delivery for their patients. The determination of nursing care that is required should be made with accurate and timely assessment of the current patient needs in collaboration with the patient's family, providers, and the healthcare team. With this assessment and consideration in place, the registered nurse may delegate certain nursing tasks to unlicensed individuals.

What can be delegated?

Not all nursing tasks may be delegated. The nurse must first determine if the task can be delegated using criteria set forth in Michigan law, in professional standards and in assessment of the unique characteristics of the individual requiring nursing services. A nursing task may be determined to be delegable and assigned to be performed by nursing assistive personnel (UAP) under the supervision of a registered nurse (RN) if the individual situation meets all of the criteria and in the nurse's judgment, it is safe to do so. It is important to note that a specific task may only be delegated for a specific patient; therefore, a procedure that is delegable for one patient may not necessarily be appropriate for any other patient and should be based on current patient assessment. Michigan law does not delineate which nursing tasks can be delegated; delegation is based on the nurse's assessment and judgment.

Licensed personnel versus unlicensed assistive personnel (UAP)

Examples of licensed personnel that the RN may supervise and delegate to include licensed practical nurses (LPNs).

Examples of unlicensed assistive personnel (UAPs) that the RN may supervise or delegate to include nursing aides, orderlies, medical assistants, attendants and technicians.

Medical assistants in Michigan are not required to possess a certification, registration or license. While the state does not require a license or certification, they may need to obtain certification to get a job or a promotion as a medical assistant.

Certified nursing assistants or aides provide patients with basic care and assist with daily living activities. Their education includes completing a training program with classroom lectures and supervised patient-care instruction.

Michigan Certified Nurse Aides (CNAs) are UAPs under the jurisdiction of the Long Term Care Division of the Department of Licensing and Regulatory Affairs (LARA, 2021).

Supervision of Delegation

In delegation between the registered nurse and UAP, supervision of the UAP is required. Supervision is defined in the Occupational Regulation Sections of the Michigan Public Health Code, Act 368 of 1978, Article 15, Part 161, General Provisions as the licensed health professional overseeing the work of another individual. This requires that the licensed health professional provide supervision. The RN must fulfill the requirement for continuous availability to the UAP and situation. Occupational Regulation Sections of the Michigan Public Health Code, Act 368 of 1978, Article 15, Part 161, General Provisions, 333.16215 ties delegation to supervision. A nurse cannot delegate without supervising.

National Guidelines for Delegation

There are National Guidelines for Nursing Delegation set forth by the National Councils of the State Boards of Nursing (NCSBN) and the American Nurses Association (ANA). The nursing delegation process as defined by NCSBN and ANA (2019) is based on research findings and evidence in the literature and is applicable to all levels of nursing licensure (advanced practice registered nurse [APRN], registered nurse [RN], licensed practical/vocational nurse [LPN/VN]) where the nurse practice act (NPA) is silent. In Michigan, nurses do not follow a Nurse Practice Act (NPA) and should instead follow both the national standards and the Michigan State Board of Nursing Rules. (ANA-NCSBN, 2019)

The national guidelines as set forth by NCSBN and ANA can be applied to:

■ APRNs when delegating to RNs, LPN/VNs and assistive personnel (AP)

■ RNs when delegating to LPN/VNs and AP

■ LPN/VNs (as allowed by their state/jurisdiction) when delegating to AP.

ote: These guidelines do not apply to the transfer of responsibility for care of a patient between licensed health are providers (e.g., RN to another RN or LPN/VN to another LPN/VN), which is considered a handoff (Agency r Healthcare Research and Quality, 2015).

CSBN and ANA have developed the 5 Rights of Delegation to guide delegation decision making:

Right task:

The activity falls within the delegatee's job description or is included as part of the established written policies and procedures of the nursing practice setting. The facility needs to ensure the policies and procedures describe the expectations and limits of the activity and provide any necessary competency training.

Right circumstance:

The health condition of the patient must be stable. If the patient's condition changes, the delegatee must communicate this to the licensed nurse, and the licensed nurse must reassess the situation and the appropriateness of the delegation.

Right person:

The licensed nurse along with the employer and the delegatee is responsible for ensuring that the delegatee possesses the appropriate skills and knowledge to perform the activity.

Right directions and communication:

Each delegation situation should be specific to the patient, the licensed nurse and the delegatee. The licensed nurse is expected to communicate specific instructions for the delegated activity to the delegatee; the delegatee, as part of two-way communication, should ask any clarifying questions. This communication includes any data that need to be collected, the method or collecting the data, the time frame for reporting the results to the licensed nurse, and additional information pertinent to the situation. The delegatee must understand the terms of the delegation and must agree to accept the delegated activity. The licensed nurse should ensure that the delegatee understands that she or he cannot make any decisions or modifications in carrying out the activity without first consulting the licensed nurse.

Right supervision and evaluation:

The licensed nurse is responsible for monitoring the delegated activity, following up with the delegatee at the completion of the activity, and evaluating patient outcomes. The delegatee is responsible for communicating patient information to the licensed nurse during the delegation situation. The licensed nurse should be ready and available to intervene as necessary. The licensed nurse should ensure appropriate documentation of the activity is completed.

Source: NCSBN. (1995, 1996)

The decision to delegate or assign is based upon the RN's judgment concerning the condition of the patient, the competence of all members of the nursing team and the degree of supervision that will be required of the RN if a task is delegated. The difference between delegation and assignment has been a source of debate for years.

Summary of Delegation

- ONLY an RN may delegate nursing acts, functions or tasks.
- LPNs may not delegate.
- LPNs must be supervised by the RN, physician, or dentist.
- The RN delegates tasks - not responsibility/accountability for patient care.
- The RN delegates from their scope of practice.
- The RN cannot delegate acts/tasks/functions that are not within their scope of practice.
- The RN determines whether the delegatee has the knowledge/skill to do a specific task.
- The RN determines whether the task for a specific client can be performed safely and competently for the specific client.
- The RN supervises the performance.
- The RN retains ultimate responsibility for the delivery and execution of safe patient care.

Michigan Public Health Code: Delegation

The Michigan State Board of Nursing allows safe delegation of nursing tasks to unlicensed persons in the Occupational Regulation Sections of the Michigan Public Health Code, Act 368 of 1978, Part 172 Nursing. The law authorizes the RN to delegate nursing activities and requires that the RN teach and supervise less skilled personnel in the performance of delegated nursing activities.

The Michigan Board of Nursing has adopted general rules regarding delegation within nursing. The Rule (R 338.10104) on Delegation is as follows:

Rule 104.

(1) Only a registered nurse may delegate nursing acts, functions, or tasks. A registered nurse who delegates nursing acts, functions, or tasks shall do all of the following:

   (a) Determine whether the act, function, or task delegated is within the registered nurse's scope of practice.

   (b) Determine the qualifications of the delegatee before such delegation.

   (c) Determine whether the delegatee has the necessary knowledge and skills for the acts, functions, or tasks to be carried out safely and competently.

   (d) Supervise and evaluate the performance of the delegatee.

   (e) Provide or recommend remediation of the performance when indicated.

(2) The registered nurse shall bear ultimate responsibility for the performance of nursing acts, functions, or tasks performed by the delegatee within the scope of the delegation (Michigan Legislature, 2021).

Michigan's Mental Health Code

The Michigan Mental Health Code is a compilation of laws intended to protect and promote the health and well-being of Michigan residents who have mental health disorders or developmental disability. It sets standards for nurses and other mental health professionals and for agencies providing mental health services.

Mental health boards provide a wide range of services, including programs for persons with serious and persistent mental health disorders, developmental disabilities and substance use disorders.

Registered nurses and especially advanced practice nurses are often in the role of mental health care delivery and support, and increased knowledge of the regulation of the area of mental health services benefits patients and their families throughout all care delivery specialties. Other health care professionals involved with mental health services include social workers, psychologists, psychiatrists, general and family health practitioners, counselors, therapists and other clinicians.

Families are specifically referenced and emphasized in the code. The definition of a family member includes a parent, step-parent, spouse, sibling, child or grandparent of a primary client. Families must be treated with dignity and respect, must be able to obtain accurate and appropriate information surrounding care choices and delivery, and should also understand the parameters of information necessary for treatment by mental health professionals. The mental health professional has an obligation to provide patient and family education to best inform decision making and appropriate care choices.

When the patient receives mental health services, Michigan's Mental Health Code, as well as other laws, serve to safeguard the patient's rights. Health professionals are responsible to protect patient rights before, during and after the provision of services to the patient.

The Mental Health Code, 1974 P.A. 258, 1995, P.A. 290, MCL 330.1001 et seq., is designed to empower patients and their families with mental health disorders, to improve overall accountability and quality of care delivery, and to provide structure and authority for community mental health service programs.

The following is a list of each section of the Michigan Mental Health Code. A description and abbreviated summary of sections most relevant to health professionals is provided when warranted.

Michigan Mental Health Code: Act 258 of 1974

AN ACT to codify, revise, consolidate, and classify the laws relating to mental health; to prescribe the powers and duties of certain state and local agencies and officials and certain private agencies and individuals; to regulate certain agencies and facilities providing mental health or substance use disorder services; to provide for certain charges and fees; to establish civil admission procedures for individuals with mental illness, substance use disorder, or developmental disability; to establish guardianship procedures for individuals with developmental disability; to establish procedures regarding individuals with mental illness, substance use disorder, or developmental disability who are in the criminal justice system; to provide for penalties and remedies; and to repeal acts and parts of acts. Imd. Eff. June 24, 2014

The code is maintained by the Legislative Service Bureau, which compiles and publishes state laws.

Michigan's Behavioral Health and Developmental Disabilities Administration (BHDDA)

The **Behavioral Health and Developmental Disabilities Administration (BHDDA)** is located within the Michigan Department of Health and Human Services (MDHHS).

The Behavioral Health and Developmental Disabilities Administration carries out responsibilities specified in the Michigan Mental Health Code (Public Act 258 of 1974 as amended) and the Michigan Public Health Code (Public Act 368 of 1978 as amended). It also administers Medicaid waivers for people with developmental disabilities, mental health disorders and serious emotional disturbance and it administers prevention and treatment services for substance use disorders. The administration establishes the policy directions and standards for the statewide system including Community Mental Health Services Programs (CMHSP) services to children and adults, substance use disorder prevention and treatment, autism services to children and families, problem gambling addictions services and state hospital centers.

The Behavioral Health and Developmental Disabilities Administration (BHDDA) services and supports in Michigan are delivered through county-based community mental health services programs (CMHSPs). Michigan Department of Health and Human Services (MDHHS), along with 46 regional Community Mental Health Services Programs (CMHSPs) and 10 Pre-paid Inpatient Health Plans (PIHPs), contracts public funds for mental health, substance abuse prevention and treatment, and developmental disability services. Medicaid funds, which are paid on a per Medicaid-eligible capitated basis, are contracted thru Prepaid Inpatient Health Plans (PIHPs), three of which are single county Pre-paid Inpatient Health Plans (PIHPs) and seven of which are regional entities. Substance Abuse services are purchased through the 10 Pre-paid Inpatient Health Plans (PIHPs) and delivered through local Recovery Oriented Systems of Care.

Each region is required to have an extensive array of services that allows for maximizing choice and control on the part of individuals in need of service. Individual plans of service are developed using a person-centered planning process for adults and family driven and youth guided services for children. Outpatient mental health services are available through Medicaid Health Plans (MHPs) for persons who are not eligible for Medicaid services through Pre-paid Inpatient Health Plans (PIHPs) and their Community Mental Health (CMH) networks.

Mental Health Treatment: Patient Rights

Right to Ask Questions and Receive Information

The patient is encouraged to ask questions about treatment and about their rights and to make suggestions that they feel are in their best interest. If the patient believes their patient rights have been violated, the patient should inform the Rights Officer/Advisor at the location where the patient is receiving services.

When the patient makes a request for, or begins to receive, mental health services, the patient to be given information about the rights guaranteed in Chapters 7 and 7A of the Mental Health Code.

the patient receives services from a community mental health services program, the patient or the patient's family should also be given information regarding available resources, advocacy and support groups, and other relevant information, including how to contact Michigan Protection and Advocacy Services.

The Michigan Department of Health and Human Services has established a 'warmline' for persons with mental health conditions. The warmline can be used ahead of crisis, as opposed to a hot line for emergencies. The warmline will be operated by Certified Peer Support Specialists. Individuals calling the warmline will be provided with support by peers who have their own lived experience with mental health issues. They will be providing wellness supports and a listening ear (MDHHS, 2021). The current phone number is 1-888-733-7753.

Right to Self Determination & Competency

The patient will continue to be treated as competent unless a court has decided that the patient is legally incompetent and has appointed a guardian for the patient. A guardian is authorized by a judge to make certain decisions for the patient. For some people, a guardian makes major decisions; for others, the guardian decides only those specific things listed in a court order. The patient must give informed consent to receive treatment or have their confidential information shared with others by the healthcare agency. In order to be able to give informed consent the patient must have:

KNOWLEDGE - The patient must be told about the risks, benefits, and available alternatives to a course of treatment or medication.

UNDERSTANDING -The patient must be able to reasonably understand the information the patient is given including the risks, benefits, available options or alternatives, or other consequences.

VOLUNTARY - The patient decision to provide consent must be voluntary. The patient should not be forced or pressured into a decision. Unless the patient is a minor or has a guardian, the choice the patient makes should be the patient.

DIGNITY AND RESPECT - The law requires all mental health service providers to assure that the patient is treated with dignity and respect. Examples of staff not showing respect include calling the patient names, making fun of the patient, teasing, or harassing the patient. The patient's family members also have the right to be treated with dignity and respect.

ACCESS TO INFORMATION - The patient has the right to see the patient treatment record. Upon request, the patient or the patient legal representative may read or get a copy of all or part of the patient record. There may be a charge for the cost of copying. If the patient is an adult and the court has not judged the patient incompetent (appointed a guardian for the patient), information entered in the patient record after March 28, 1996 may not be withheld from the patient under any circumstances.

FREEDOM FROM DISCRIMINATION - Title II of the Americans with Disabilities Act (ADA) prohibits discrimination on the basis of disability by public entities. It states that people with disabilities cannot be denied services or participation in programs or activities that are available to people without disabilities. If the patient feels her or his rights under Title II have been violated by state or local governmental agencies, the patient may file a complaint with the Department of Justice.

Michigan Behavioral Health Standard Consent Form

In 2015, the Michigan Department of Health and Human Services released a standard consent form for the sharing of health information specific to behavioral health and substance use treatment. In Michigan, all providers are required to accept this new standard form (MDHHS, 2021).

Rights of Minors

If the patient is a minor between 14 and 17, the patient has the right to ask for, and receive, outpatient mental health services (not including psychotropic medication or pregnancy termination referral services) without the consent or knowledge of the patient parent or guardian. These services are limited to 12 sessions or 4 months for each request.

The health professional should consult the institution's legal representation when the wishes of parents are in conflict with the minor's wishes, when the minor is emancipated, or when any conflict between the health care team and family occurs.

Mental Health Treatment:
Involuntary Admission Process

Involuntary Admission: Petition or Application

The State of Michigan Probate Court has set guidelines for the family member or health professional to petition for the involuntary admission process of an individual for mental health services. In order for a person to be involuntarily hospitalized, she or he must meet the Michigan Mental Health Code definition of a "person requiring treatment." A person may be seriously mentally ill and still not fit that definition. A petition shall have been executed not more than 10 days before the presentation of the individual to the hospital. (MCL Act 320, eff. Feb. 14, 2017).

The individual must meet one of three criteria in addition to a mental health disorder:

- The individual has mental illness and as a result of that mental illness, the individual can reasonably be expected within the near future to intentionally or unintentionally seriously physically injure self or others, and has engaged in an act or acts or made significant threats that are substantially supportive of this expectation.

- As a result of mental illness, the individual is unable to attend to those basic physical needs that must be attended to in order to avoid serious harm in the near future, and has demonstrated that inability by failing to attend to those basic physical needs.

- The individual's judgment is so impaired by that mental illness and his or her lack of understanding of the need for treatment has caused him or her to demonstrate an unwillingness to voluntarily participate in or adhere to treatment that is necessary, on the basis of competent clinical opinion, to prevent a relapse or harmful deterioration of his or her condition, and presents a substantial risk of significant physical or mental harm to the individual or others (Form PCM 201, MCL 330.1100a(29), MCL 330.1401, MCL 330.1423, MCL 330.1427, MCL 330.1434, MCL 330.1438, MCL 330.2050, MCR 5.125(C)(18); Revised May 2021).

Involuntary Admission Process: Certification for Admission

As well as the petition or application, the patient must have a medical evaluation and certification that meets one of the following criteria:

- a clinical certificate by a physician or licensed psychologist taken within the last 72 hours
- a clinical certificate by a psychiatrist taken within the last 72 hours
- no clinical certificate is necessary because only assisted outpatient treatment is requested.

The clinical certificate in Michigan is only good for 72 hours.

The treatment order can be a combination of factors, including:

- hospitalization only.
- a combination of hospitalization and assisted outpatient treatment
- assisted outpatient treatment without hospitalization (see 'Kevin's Law' below)
- a request for the individual to be hospitalized pending a hearing

After a petition and certification, the individual will be transported to the preadmission screening unit or hospital designated by the community mental health services program for hospitalization under Mental Health Code Section 423. If the individual taken to a preadmission screening unit meets the requirements for hospitalization, then unless the community mental health services program makes other transportation arrangements, the individual will be transported by a peace officer to a treatment hospital designated by the community mental health services program (MCL Act 320, 2/2017).

A hospital designated under section 422 shall receive and detain an individual presented for not more than 24 hours. During that time the individual shall be examined by a physician or a licensed psychologist unless a clinical certificate has already been presented to the hospital. If the examining physician or psychologist does not certify that the individual is a person requiring treatment, the individual shall be released immediately. If the examining physician or psychologist executes a clinical certificate, the individual may be hospitalized under section 423 of the Mental Health Code.

Kevin's Law: Protection for Temporary Impaired Judgment

Kevin's Law helps provide protection and care for individuals whose mental illness has temporarily impaired their judgment about the need for treatment. The law allows a court to order "Assisted Outpatient Treatment" for people with mental illness who are "least able to help themselves or most likely to present a risk to others." This law does not apply to people who have a drug or alcohol problem, unless they also have a mental illness. Kevin's Law took effect in March 2005 in Michigan.

Involuntary Admission Rights

If the patient is INVOLUNTARILY ADMITTED (COURT ORDERED) to a psychiatric hospital or unit, the patient has the following rights:

- To make at least two phone calls.
- To a copy of the application or petition saying the patient require treatment and to copies of reports by the doctors who examine the patient.
- To have a physical and mental examination within 24 hours after the patient are admitted, and again at least once a year.
- To a written statement explaining that the patient will be examined by a psychiatrist within 24 hours after the patient are admitted.
- To a written statement explaining the patient rights.
- To a full court hearing.
- To be represented by an attorney.
- To be present at the hearing.
- To a jury trial.
- To an independent clinical examination.
- To have staff, if the patient wishes, notify the patient's family of the admission to the hospital.
- If the police take the patient into protective custody and bring the patient to a preadmission screening unit, to have staff of that unit complete their examination of the patient within two (2) hours unless there is a documented medical reason for the delay.
- To be examined by two doctors or by a psychologist and a psychiatrist to determine whether the patient needs to be admitted. One of the examinations must be by a psychiatrist and the first examination may be done before the patient is brought to the hospital.

■ To refuse medication before the patient court hearing unless a physician decides the patient needs it to prevent the patient from physically hurting himself or herself or others or if the patient's life is in danger.

Involuntary Admission: Refusal of Treatment

As an involuntary (court-ordered) recipient, the patient does not have the right to refuse treatment. However, the patient does have the right to ask questions about the patient treatment, participate in the development of the patient plan of service, and discuss it with the patient doctor or other mental health professionals. If the patient thinks the patient treatment is not helping, the patient may ask for a review of the patient treatment plan.

Workplace Rights for All Nurses

Most nurses are employed either as "at will" or union employees. At will employees are those persons who are employed at the will of their employers and without a collective bargaining agreement (union contract). Although many nurses confuse employee handbooks with employee contracts, the courts have widely held that handbooks do not constitute contracts. Union nurses as employees are persons who are organized into one collective bargaining unit and who work under a legally binding contract. Employees who are members of a collective bargaining unit have additional rights by virtue of their status in an organized union. Some laws apply to both types of employees; other laws apply only to union employees. The following section summarizes selected laws that affect all professional nurses as employees. The last section discusses additional laws that pertain to nurses in collective bargaining.

Americans with Disabilities Act (ADA)

The Americans with Disabilities Act (ADA) is an equal opportunity law modeled after the Civil Rights Act of 1964, which prohibits discrimination on the basis of race, color, religion, sex, or national origin. Title I of the ADA prohibits private employers, state and local governments, employment agencies and labor unions from discriminating against qualified individuals with disabilities in job application procedures, hiring, firing, advancement, job assignments, pay, benefits, job training, and other employment practices. (ADA, 2020)

This part of the law also requires that employers and other specified persons and organizations provide reasonable accommodation for a known disability of a qualified applicant or employee at their request and if it would not impose an "undue hardship" on the operations of the employer's business. A disability, according to the ADA, is defined as a physical or mental impairment that substantially limits one or more major life activities, a person who has a history or record of such an impairment, or a person who is perceived by others as having such an impairment. (ADA, 2020)

Fair Labor Standards Act (FLSA)

The Fair Labor Standards Act (FLSA) establishes minimum wage, overtime pay, recordkeeping and child labor standards affecting full-time and part-time workers in the private sector and in federal, state and local governments. (U.S. Dept. of Labor, n.d.)

Overtime Requirements: Covered nonexempt employees must receive overtime pay at a rate of not less than one and one-half times their regular rate of pay for hours worked over 40 hours per workweek (any fixed and regularly reoccurring period of 168 hours - seven consecutive 24-hour periods). Nonexempt employees are individuals who are not exempt from the overtime provisions of the FLSA and is therefore entitled to overtime pay for all hours worked beyond 40 in a workweek (as well as any state overtime provisions). Nonexempt employees may be paid on a salary, hourly or other basis. In the healthcare industry the requirements may be changed by agreement with the employees or their union to overtime pay at one and one-half times the employee's regular rate of pay for all hours worked over a regular shift length, normal scheduled hours in a workday and 80 hours in a 14-day work period, or as defined either contractually or by the employer.

Hour Limits: The FLSA does not impose a limit on the number of hours employees older than 16 may work in a week, nor does it require premium pay for weekends or holidays, unless the overtime thresholds identified above are met.

Rest and Meal Periods: The FLSA recognizes both but does not require either. A rest period is customarily 5 to 20 minutes and employees must be paid for the break and the break must be treated as "hours worked" for overtime computation purposes. "Bona fide" meal periods, on the other hand, need not be compensated or treated as "hours worked" for overtime purposes provided they are:

- of sufficient duration (30 minutes or longer is customary)
- it is free and uninterrupted - employees must be completely relieved of duties. Nurses often do not receive free and uninterrupted meal periods and should be compensated, including overtime compensation when warranted, for missed or interrupted meal periods.

Suffered or Permitted to Work: The FLSA requires an employer to compensate employees for any work that it allows to occur. Management cannot sit back and accept the benefits of an employee's services and not provide compensation. This principle can come into play when a nurse feels pressure to clock out and then continue to work after the end of the shift. This time is compensable under the FLSA even if the employer did not specifically authorize the nurse to continue working, so long as the employer knows or has reason to believe this practice is occurring.

FLSA Minimums: The FLSA establishes minimum standards. Union contracts often provide additional premium pay and overtime benefits above the FLSA minimums. (U.S. Dept. of Labor, n.d.)

Family and Medical Leave Act (FMLA)

The Family and Medical Leave Act (FMLA) provides certain employees with up to 12 work weeks of unpaid, job-protected leave each year, and requires group health benefits to be maintained during the leave, as if employees continued to work instead of taking leave. To qualify, the nurse must work for an employer with 50 or more employees and meet one of the five categories of eligibility for FMLA:

- An employee who has a baby and cares for the baby.
- A baby or child is placed with the employee for adoption or foster care.
- The employee must care for a spouse, child or parent if there is a serious health condition.

- The employee has a serious health condition that makes the employee unable to perform the functions of their job.
- Any qualifying exigency arising out of the fact that the employee's spouse, son, daughter or parent is a covered military member on "covered active duty" or 26 work weeks of leave during a single 12-month period to care for a covered service member with a serious injury or illness, if the eligible employee is the service members spouse, son, daughter, parent or next of kin (military caregiver leave).

he 12 work weeks of FMLA do not have to be taken concurrently (U.S. Dept. of Labor, n.d.).

Occupational Safety and Health Act (OSHA)

1970, Congress created the Occupational Safety and Health Administration (OSHA) to ensure safe and ealthful working conditions for workers by setting and enforcing standards and by providing training, outreach, ducation and assistance (U.S. Dept. of Labor, n.d.).

ederal law entitles employees to a safe workplace. The employer must keep the workplace free of known ealth and safety hazards. Employees have the right to speak up about hazards without fear of retaliation. mployees also have the right to:

- Receive workplace safety and health training in a language he/she understands
- Work on machines that are safe
- Receive required safety equipment, such as gloves or a harness and lifeline for falls
- Be protected from toxic chemicals
- Request an OSHA inspection, and speak to the inspector
- Report an injury or illness, and get copies of personal medical records
- Review records of work-related injuries and illnesses
- See results of tests taken to find workplace hazards (U.S. Dept. of Labor, n.d.)

The Health Facility Whistleblower's Protection Act (WPA)

he Whistleblowers Act for health care workers broadens the scope of the original Whistleblower Protection Act WPA). The coverage is no longer confined to a violation of law/ regulation/rule. Health care workers are now ble to report an "unsafe practice or condition" which is not a violation of the public health code or any other law.

hospital employee or contractor is immune from civil or criminal liability that might otherwise be incurred-- and hall not be discharged, threatened, or otherwise discriminated against by the hospital regarding that person's ompensation or the terms, conditions, location, or privileges of that person's employment-- if that person eports to the Department of Health and Human Services verbally or in writing, an issue related to the hospital at is an unsafe practice or condition that is not a violation of hospital licensing laws.

nless the person is required by law to report earlier, a hospital employee or contractor is eligible for this nmunity and protection only if they meet both of the following conditions before reporting to the unsafe practice r condition that is not a violation of hospital licensing laws:

- The person must give the hospital 60 days' written notice of the unsafe practice or condition. (Within 60 days after receiving a written notice, the hospital must provide a written response to the person who provided the notice)
- The person had no reasonable expectation that the hospital had taken or would take timely action to address the issue related to the hospital that is an unsafe practice or condition (U.S. Dept. of Labor, n.d.)

Health Insurance Portability and Accountability Act Privacy Rule (HIPAA)

HIPAA provides rights over personal health information and sets rules and limits on who can look at and receive an individual's health information. HIPAA applies to all forms of protected health information, whether electronic, written or oral.

In some cases, nurses can access health information to:

- ■ Provide treatment and care coordination.
- ■ Share information with family, relatives, friends or others that an individual identifies as a person involved with his or her health care.
- ■ Protect the public's health, such as reporting when flu is in the area.
- ■ Make required reports to the police, such as reporting gunshot wounds.
- ■ Provide emergency care when the patient is unresponsive but is carrying medical information with them (HHS, 2020)

Consolidated Omnibus Budget Reconciliation Act (COBRA)

The Consolidated Omnibus Budget Reconciliation Act (COBRA) gives workers and their families who lose their health benefits the right to choose to continue group health benefits provided by their group health plan for limited periods of time under certain circumstances such as voluntary or involuntary job loss, reduction in the hours worked, transition between jobs, death, divorce, and other life events.

Qualified individuals may be required to pay the entire premium for coverage up to 102 percent of the cost to the plan. COBRA generally requires that group health plans sponsored by employers with 20 or more employees in the prior year offer employees and their families the opportunity for a temporary extension of health coverage (called continuation coverage) in certain instances where coverage under the plan would otherwise end. COBRA outlines how employees and family members may elect continuation coverage. It also requires employers and plans to provide notice (U.S. Dept. of Labor Seal, n.d.)

Bullard-Plawecki Right to Know Act

The Bullard-Plawecki Right to Know Act gives employees the right to periodically review their personnel record, prescribes the conditions under which a review and copying of a personnel record shall take place, limits the employer's rights to retain and disclose certain personnel information, and allows an employee to include a written rebuttal to any document in their personnel record (Michigan Legislature, 1978).

Needlestick Safety and Prevention Act

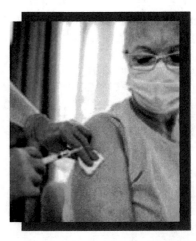

The Needlestick Safety and Prevention Act was signed into law on November 6, 2000. The law modifies the federal Bloodborne Pathogen Standards under the Occupational Safety and Health Administration (OSHA) to require the use of "sharps with engineered sharps injury protection features" and "needleless systems" to reduce the incidence of accidental sharps injuries in health care settings.

The federal law requires non-management employee input in identifying, evaluating and selecting the products to be used. Employers are required to update and review their exposure control plan to reflect changes in technology.

dditionally, the employer is required to maintain a sharps injury log which will include, at a minimum, the pe and brand of device involved in the incident, the department or work area where the exposure incident ccurred, and an explanation of how the incident occurred (Tatelbaum, 2001).

Workers' Disability Compensation Act (Michigan)

he Michigan Workers' Disability Compensation Act provides remedial relief and benefits for persons injured nd disabled as a result of injuries, illnesses, or diseases connected with the workplace. Workers' compensation a no-fault system that allows workers to receive benefits and requires employers to pay benefits regardless the fault causing the disability. The Act provides benefits to all employees who are injured or disabled by onditions arising out of and in the course of employment, except for mental disabilities and conditions of the jing process. Mental disabilities and conditions of the aging process may be compensated if it is shown that e workplace was a significant contributor to the condition. Worker's compensation is a statutory system at preempts or eliminates most legal remedies regarding injuries and disabilities of the workplace. The Act ovides for a Workers' Compensation Agency to administer the Act and provide remedies. All claims must be andled by the Agency (Workers' Disability Compensation Agency, n.d.)

Unemployment Insurance (Michigan)

he Michigan Unemployment Insurance program is mandated by federal law and administered in Michigan by e Unemployment Insurance Agency (UIA). This program assists individuals by providing temporary income hile they actively seek new employment. An employee can receive benefits each week they are unemployed r up to 20 weeks. Unemployment benefits may be applied for the week following the last week at work. To e eligible for unemployment benefits, a person must be unemployed and able to, available for and actively eeking suitable full-time work. Unless instructed otherwise by the Unemployment Insurance Agency staff, e individual must also register for work at two to three businesses before pursuing unemployment. Michigan Vorks! agencies help workers in Michigan create a Pure Michigan Talent Connect profile to assist them in finding ork Locations can be found at www.michiganworks.org. (Labor and Economic Opportunity - Unemployment surance Agency, n.d.).

Mandatory Overtime Resolution

olicy can also be made through the resolution process. A resolution is a document expressing the will of e House or the Senate (or both, in the case of concurrent resolutions). Resolutions are used to urge state gencies or the Congress to take certain actions; to formally approve certain plans of governmental agencies; conduct certain legislative business; or to establish study committees to examine issues. Sometimes this an work simultaneously with attempts at legislative reform and is often a quicker process. An example is e situation with mandatory overtime. The charge is often "client abandonment" if a nurse does not work dditional time. While nurses are working for legislative solutions at the state and federal levels, employers ave threatened to report them to the Board of Nursing (BON) with subsequent loss of license if they do not omply with mandated overtime. Nurse members of the Michigan Board of Nursing were concerned about ensure being placed in the middle of this staffing controversy and about the effect of overtime on the patient afety. They passed a resolution in 2006 indicating that the BON expected licensed nurses (LPNs and RNs) to xercise their clinical judgment in accepting or rejecting requests to work overtime based on their ability to give afe patient care. If a nurse did not believe that he/she could provide safe care, the nurse would be well within hat the BON expected in rejecting that assignment. It was acknowledged that such a rejection did not in and f itself constitute client abandonment.

his resolution was upheld by the attorney general for the state of Michigan. It meant that employers could not hreaten nurses with the loss of their licenses. A similar resolution was subsequently adopted by the delegate assembly of the National Council of State Boards of Nursing. Thus, in a relatively short span of time, nurses collaborated to bring about policy changes that meant that they could not lose their licenses for refusing to be placed in a position of providing potentially unsafe care. Unfortunately, none of these resolutions prohibit employers from firing nurses, so the need for legislative redress continues (Nagelkerk, 2006).

Unionized Nurses' Workplace Rights

The National Labor Relations Act (NLRA) gives employees the right to organize themselves into unions and to bargain collectively with their employer through representatives of the employees' choosing. Michigan Nurses Association (MNA) is the largest, most effective union for RNs. A professional union differs from a trade union in that the professional union assists the professional in defining and defending his/her practice, encourages patient advocacy, and bargains for fair wages, benefits, and working conditions, while a trade union primarily serves non-professionals and focuses almost entirely on wages, benefits, and working conditions.

Nurses represented by a union work with their union representative to negotiate a legally binding contract with their employer, outlining the terms and conditions of employment. Topics commonly include employee status, work hours, wages and related pay, fringe benefits, discipline, grievance procedure, staffing levels, health and safety, nondiscrimination, professional practice committees, in-service education, continuing education, leaves of absence, holidays, layoffs and other matters important to nurses.

The hallmark of the professional union is defining and defending the professional's practice. MNA contracts address a wide range of practice issues such as language on the role of the nurse, non-nursing duties, staffing, scheduling practices, professional practice committees, measurement of quality indicators, and tuition reimbursement.

As a result of collective bargaining, nurses have a mechanism for resolving contract-related issues through a formal grievance process. The ideal grievance procedure assures that an employee's complaint is handled fairly, quickly and without fear of retaliation. A key element in a fair grievance procedure is the orderly series of steps, progressing upward through successively higher levels of administration and ending in binding arbitration. Time schedules for handling grievances may vary from contract to contract, but the ultimate objective is to expedite the grievance as quickly as possible. In general, unionized employees have legally protected rights regarding their employment.

While contracts vary significantly, nurses who are in a professional union also have mechanisms for participating in decisions that affect their practice, their patients and themselves as employees. Union represented nurses enjoy certain legal rights that non-union nurses do not have. One such mechanism is described below:

Weingarten Rights

The 1975 U.S. Supreme Court case National Labor Relations Board (NLRB) v. J. Weingarten ruled that an employee represented for collective bargaining has the right to have a union representative present during any interview conducted by a management official that may result in discipline. This rule helps protect the nurse's ense and employment. The nurse must make the request for a union representative; the employer does not ave to remind the nurse of this union right.

Shown below is a standard statement used when invoking Weingarten rights:

WEINGARTEN RIGHTS

I believe this discussion could lead to my being disciplined. I therefore request that my union representative or officer be present to assist me at the meeting. I further request reasonable time to consult with my union representative regarding the subject and purpose of the meeting. Please consider this a continuing request; without representation, I shall not participate in the discussion. I SHALL NOT CONSENT TO ANY SEARCHES OR TESTS affecting my person, property, or effects without first consulting with my union representative.

Disciplinary Action and the Bureau of Professional Licensing

Allegations of improper performance or activities by nurses are serious charges. The Michigan Bureau of Professional Licensing (BPL) within the Department of Licensing and Regulatory Affairs (LARA) receives and investigates such allegations to determine if they are valid.

Nurses who are investigated by the Bureau of Health Professions often do not know where to turn for advocacy. The Bureau and the Board of Nursing are charged with a responsibility to investigate allegations and advocate for the public in the investigatory process. They are not advocates for the nurse. Nurses under investigation are advised to seek legal counsel.

When can a nurse be investigated for possible disciplinary action?

The Bureau of Professional Licensing may investigate any individual licensed by the Board of Nursing if that person is believed to be incompetent, has been criminally convicted of an offense relating to her/his practice, is guilty of fraud, is unable to provide safe and competent care to patients, or has violated other provisions of the Michigan Public Health Code.

Allegations involving substance abuse or mental or physical impairment will be referred to Michigan's Health Professional Recovery Program (HPRP) which will attempt to initiate a treatment-oriented non-disciplinary approach to address the individual's impairment.

Who may request an investigation?

Any citizen may file an allegation with LARA if they believe a licensed health professional has violated the Public Health Code. The allegation must include the name and contact information of the individual making the report, be in writing, include the name of the licensed individual and include details related to the incident being reported. The department has an allegation form on its website, https://www.michigan.gov/lara/0,4601,7-154-89334_72600_73836---,00.html that can be used.

Anonymous complaints are discouraged and may result in the complaint being closed, as the investigator would be unable to ask for information, records, etc. The identity of the person filing a complaint is confidential and may only be disclosed if the person provides a written release of his/her name and information to be shared. If the matter proceeds to an administrative hearing, disclosure may be requested from the complainant (LARA, n.d.).

What happens after a complaint is filed against a licensed health professional?

The complaint is reviewed to determine if a possible violation of the Public Health Code has occurred. Based on this review, the Bureau of Professional Licensing (BPL) will do one of the following:

- Request authorization to investigate the complaint from the appropriate health professional board.

- Close the complaint with no further action due to the complaint not being associated with a possible violation of the Public Health Code.

- Close and refer the matter to another state agency or entity if the complaint is not within the jurisdiction of BPL/LARA.

NOTE: LARA may work with law enforcement, the Attorney General's Office, MDHHS and other agencies depending on the nature of the complaint (LARA, n.d.).

What happens during a complaint investigation?

During an investigation based on a complaint, BPL investigators will interview relevant parties and collect evidence related to the complaint. BPL's investigations are independent of any other investigation of a licensee, such as one by their employer or law enforcement (LARA, n.d.).

What happens after a complaint investigation is completed?

If it is determined from the investigation that a violation of the Public Health Code cannot be substantiated, BPL will close the complaint file and notify the complainant. If it is determined that a violation of the Public Health Code has occurred, BPL will file an administrative complaint against the licensee. Depending on the nature of the case, BPL has the authority to summarily suspend a license if the public health, safety, or welfare requires emergency action (LARA, n.d.).

What options does the licensee have after an administrative complaint is filed?

Once an administrative complaint is issued to a licensee, the licensee may do any of the following:

- Respond and admit to the facts of the administrative complaint and agree to a Consent Order. The matter will proceed to the appropriate board for sanctions.

- Seek a compliance conference with BPL to discuss and possibly settle the matter. This is an opportunity for the licensee to reach a settlement without having to address the issue at an administrative hearing. This may result in a licensee being sanctioned, which could include being fined, placed on probation, or suspended from practice.

If an agreement is reached, the proposed settlement must be approved by the disciplinary subcommittee (DSC) of the appropriate licensing board before it becomes final. If a settlement is not reached or if the DSC rejects the proposed settlement, the case proceeds to an administrative hearing.

- Request a hearing with the Michigan Office of Administrative Hearings & Rules (MOAHR) for an Administrative Law Judge (ALJ) to determine the facts of the case and prepare a Proposal for Decision (PFD). The case would then go to the DSC for approval or rejection of the ALJ's decision and for sanctions. An administrative hearing is held to determine the facts of the case, what laws or rules apply, and whether the health professional violated the Public Health Code. After the hearing, the administrative law judge submits a PFD regarding the hearing for review and determination by the appropriate DSC.

- Not respond, at which point the licensee is in default and the case moves through the process and is sent to the appropriate board for action (LARA, n.d.).

Who determines the final action(s) against the license of the health professional?

The ultimate determination of whether a health professional licensee violated the Public Health Code is made by the Disciplinary Subcommittee (DSC) of the health profession board. The DSC has the option of dismissing the Administrative Complaint or finding a violation of the Public Health Code and taking the disciplinary action against the license of the health care professional as provided under the Public Health Code (LARA, n.d.).

Is the decision of the DSC final?

The licensee may appeal the decision of the DSC with the Michigan Court of Appeals (LARA, n.d.).

Disciplinary Action Procedure and Nursing Role Responsibility

As well as delineation of role parameters and expected licensure framework, there are specific steps that precede suspension or revocation of a nursing license. An additional function of professional licensing boards is to outline a process of accountability and discipline is necessary for licensees under their jurisdiction.

Disciplinary Action

Activities of the governmental branch charged with carrying it out: Nursing disciplinary action is an example of interpretation of the law by the Michigan Board of Nursing (BON). The BON has implemented a series of steps in the disciplinary process including how to report a suspected violation that may be connected to negligence or malpractice, screening of potential violations, investigation and also conducting a hearing (Michigan Legislature, 2021).

Overview of Negligence and Malpractice

Negligence: Negligence is the act of a failure to behave with the level of care that someone of ordinary prudence would have exercised under the same circumstances. The behavior usually consists of actions, but can also consist of omissions when there is some duty to act (e.g., a duty to help victims of one's previous conduct) (Cornell Legal Information Institute, 2021).

Malpractice: Medical malpractice occurs when a hospital, doctor or other health professional, through a negligent act or omission, causes an injury to a patient.

Regulatory and judicial decisions may arise subsequent to suits filed against specific practitioners or agencies on the basis of negligence or malpractice.

To be considered medical malpractice under the law, the claim must have the following characteristics:

A) The standard of care was violated

B) An injury was caused by the negligence

C) The injury resulted in significant damage

(American Board of Professional Liability Attorneys, 2021)

Mandatory Reporting of Violations

When a nurse takes action that violates the public health code, that nurse must be reported. Depending on the type of violation, different requirements exist.

Administrative Rules: Knowledge of a Violation

R 333.16222 Knowledge of violation; report to department; confidentiality of information; failure to make report; exception; identity of licensee or registrant making report; notice of criminal conviction or disciplinary action by another state.

1. A licensee or registrant having knowledge that another licensee or registrant has committed a violation under Section 16221 or Article 7 or a rule promulgated under Article 7 shall report the conduct and the name of the subject of the report to the department. Information obtained by the department under this subsection is confidential and is subject to Sections 16238 and 16244. Failure of a licensee or registrant to make a report under this subsection does not give rise to a civil cause of action for damages against the licensee or registrant, but the licensee or registrant is subject to administrative action under Sections 16221 and 16226. This subsection does not apply to a licensee or registrant who obtains the knowledge of a violation while providing professional services to the licensee or registrant to whom the knowledge applies, who is serving on a duly constituted ethics or peer review committee of a professional association, or who is serving on a committee assigned a professional review function in a health facility or agency.

2. Unless the licensee or registrant making the report otherwise agrees in writing, the identity of the licensee or registrant making the report shall remain confidential unless disciplinary proceedings under this part are initiated against the subject of the report and the licensee or registrant making the report is required to testify in the proceedings.

3. A licensee or registrant shall notify the department of a criminal conviction or a disciplinary licensing or registration action taken by another state against the licensee or registrant within 30 days after the date of the conviction or action. This subsection includes, but is not limited to, a disciplinary action that is stayed pending appeal.

Administrative Rules: Knowledge of Impairment

R 333.16223 Impairment of licensee, registrant or applicant; report; exception; liability.

1. Except as otherwise provided in this section, a licensee or registrant who has reasonable cause to believe that a licensee, registrant or applicant is impaired shall report that fact to the department. For purposes

of this subsection, a report filed with the committee or with the program consultants described in Section 16168 is considered to be filed with the department. A licensee or registrant who fails to report under this subsection is not liable in a civil action for damages resulting from the failure to report, but the licensee or registrant is subject to administrative action under Sections 16221 and 16226.

This section does not apply to a licensee or registrant who is in a bona fide health professional-patient relationship with a licensee, registrant or applicant believed to be impaired.

A licensee or registrant who in good faith complies with this section is not liable for damages in a civil action or subject to prosecution in a criminal proceeding as a result of the compliance.

Reporting Requirements of an Employer (MCL)

Employers (under this section of the act) are defined as health facilities or agencies that employ, contract with or grant privileges to a health professional licensed or registered under Article 15.

What are they required to report and to whom do they report?

Employers must report:

- When a licensee has been terminated or has resigned as the result of disciplinary action.
- When a licensee has resigned as a result of clinical privileges being restricted or revoked.
- When a licensee has resigned as a result of serious concerns about the individual's clinical competence.
- Termination of any health professional covered under this law, for any reason, by means of a report to the DCH. The exception would be someone who loses their job through downsizing.

Employers are required to report the above circumstances to the Michigan Department of Health and Human Services within 30 days of the action.

Administrative Rules: Report or notice of disciplinary action by health facility or agency

333.20175 Report or notice of disciplinary action; information provided in report; natural use of certain records, data, and knowledge.

A health facility or agency that employs, contracts with, or grants privileges to a health professional licensed or registered under Article 15 shall report the following to the Department of Health and Human Services not more than 30 days after it occurs:

a. Disciplinary action taken by the health facility or agency against a health professional licensed or registered under Article

15 based on the licensee's or registrant's professional competence, disciplinary action that results in a change of employment status, or disciplinary action based on conduct that adversely affected the licensee's or registrant's clinical privileges for a period of more than 15 days. As used in this subdivision, "adversely affects" means the reduction, restriction, suspension, revocation, denial or failure to renew the clinical privileges of a licensee or registrant by a health facility or agency.

b. Restriction or acceptance of the surrender of the clinical privileges of a licensee or registrant under either of the following circumstances:

 i. The licensee or registrant is under investigation by the health facility or agency.

ii.   There is an agreement in which the health facility or agency agrees not to conduct an investigation into the licensee's or registrant's alleged professional incompetence or improper professional conduct.

c.   A case in which a health professional resigns or terminates a contract or whose contract is not renewed instead of the health facility taking disciplinary action against the health professional.

6.   Upon request by another health facility or agency seeking a reference for purposes of changing or granting staff privileges, credentials, or employment, a health facility or agency that employs, contracts with, or grants privileges to health professionals licensed or registered under Article 15 shall notify the requesting health facility or agency of any disciplinary or other action reportable under Subsection (5) that it has taken against a health professional licensed or registered under Article 15 and employed by, under contract to, or granted privileges by the health facility or agency.

7.   For the purpose of reporting disciplinary actions pursuant to this section, a health facility or agency shall include only the following in the information provided:

a.   The name of the licensee or registrant against whom disciplinary action has been taken.

b.   A description of the disciplinary action taken.

c.   The specific grounds for the disciplinary action taken.

d.   The date of the incident that is the basis for the disciplinary action.

8.   The records, data, and knowledge collected for or by individuals or committees assigned a professional review function in a health facility or agency are confidential, shall be used only for the purposes provided in this article, are not public records, and are not subject to court subpoena.

R 333.20176a Health facility or agency; prohibited conduct; violation; fine.

1.   A health facility or agency shall not discharge or discipline, threaten to discharge or discipline, or otherwise discriminate against an employee regarding the employee's compensation, terms, conditions, location, or privileges of employment because the employee or an individual acting on behalf of the employee does either or both of the following:

a.   In good faith reports or intends to report, verbally or in writing, the malpractice of a health professional or a violation of Article 7 or Article 15 or a rule promulgated under Article 7 or Article 15.

[NOTE: Article 7 refers to the Public Health Code (P.A. 368 of 1978) section on controlled substances. Article 15 refers to the Public Health Code section on health occupations.]

b.   Acts as an expert witness in a civil action involving medical malpractice or in an administrative action.

2.   In addition to the sections set forth in Section 20165, a health facility or agency that violates subsection (1) is subject to an administrative fine of not more than $10,000.00 for each violation.

Michigan's Health Professional Recovery Program (HPRP): Treatment for health care professionals with substance use disorders

Health care professionals are required to report health professionals whom they have reasonable cause to believe may have substance use or mental health disorders. Reports are made in good faith and the reporter's name is not disclosed to the licensee. However, if there is subsequent disciplinary action against the licensee/registrant, the reporter may be contacted and may be required to testify as to what was observed (LARA-HPRP, 2021).

A health care professional with impairment due to substance use or mental health disorders may exhibit, but are not limited to, the following signs:

Change in Work Habits:

- Missing work or frequently tardy
- Failing to keep scheduled appointments
- Late submissions of reports or assignments
- Asking others to cover for hours or errors
- Unacceptable error rates
- Volunteering for drug-oriented tasks

Emotional or Behavioral Changes:

- More withdrawn socially or professionally
- More irritable, anxious, jealous, angry, depressed or moody
- More defensive - becoming angry when someone mentions their use of drugs, drinking or emotional instability
- Denying or expressing guilt or shame about personal use

Physical Changes:

- A deterioration in personal hygiene
- Changes in eating patterns or body weight
- Changes in sleeping patterns

If an individual would like to make a referral, they can contact the HPRP at 1-800-453-3784 or www.hprp.org.

HPRP Program Process

Participant confidentiality is protected as long as they are in compliance with their Monitoring Agreement. Their name will not be disclosed to the Department of Licensing and Regulatory Affairs, the licensing boards, or the public by the contractor under subpoena or a Freedom of Information Request under Section 333.16170a of the Public Health Code.

The overall process of the HPRP is to provide a structured monitoring process that coordinates services between health professionals (referred to as program participants), and approved providers. The steps of the HPRP process are:

1. **Identification of need:** participants in the HPRP program can self-report to the program or can be referred by an individual, law enforcement or their organization.

2. **Intake:** the HPRP is a confidential process that protects the individual's license while participating in the program. Intake is on a rolling calendar as the need may arise and is not limited to a specific calendar window.

3. **Referrals:** The HPRP offers participants with referral services to approved providers, known as evaluators.

4. **Evaluation:** Evaluators meet with the participant to determine whether there is a diagnosis for a substance use disorder or mental health disorder that merits monitoring. The evaluation includes, but is not limited to, the following:

   a. Evaluating symptoms, treatment needs, personal safety, and risks to the public.

   b. Reviewing the participant's history of substance use, medical and treatment history, and social and demographic information.

   c. Determining diagnosis and practice limitations.

   d. Providing treatment and recovery recommendations.

5. **Agreements:** When the evaluator determines an eligible diagnosis exists, the HPRP consults with the evaluator to develop a monitoring agreement.

   a. The monitoring agreement is a signed contract between the participant and the HPRP that is designed to monitor the participant's treatment and continuing care requirements.

   b. The agreement includes, but is not limited to, the following:
   - Requirements for remaining compliant with the program.
   - Work restrictions and conditions, if any.
   - Requirement for drug screening, if applicable.
   - Requirements pertaining to submitting self-help logs and other reports.
   - A schedule for required provider visits and group meeting attendance.

6. **Compliance:** The HPRP monitors each individual's level of participation and compliance in the program throughout the duration of the agreement. Compliance includes, but is not limited to, the following:

   a. Coordinating communication between providers, participants, and the program.

   b. Reviewing actions to be taken in the event of relapse or other incidences of noncompliance.

   c. Making necessary adjustments to monitoring agreements to address areas of noncompliance.

   d. Determining when dismissal from the program is merited.

   e. Reviewing required reports from participants and providers to determine the participant's level of compliance and progress of recovery.

Noncompliance: Due to the inherent risk to the public presented by a licensed health professional who may be impaired, participants who fail to complete the intake process or refuse to comply with the requirements of a signed monitoring agreement are reported to Michigan Health Professional Recovery Program as required by the Public Health Code. Once reported to the Department, the Department determines whether disciplinary actions will be taken (HPRP, 2021).

HPRP Participant Types

NON-REGULATORY: For participants who self-report or are referred by the Department for non-disciplinary monitoring.

REGULATORY: For participants who are referred to the HPRP under the terms of a disciplinary board order.

HPRP Treatment and Agreement Types

There are a variety of monitoring agreements used to monitor participants. Each agreement has a regulatory version and non-regulatory version.

- Substance Use Disorder (SUD): This agreement is for participants who receive an SUD diagnosis but no mental health diagnosis or indication of a pain management issue.
- Mental Health Disorder (MHD): This agreement is for participants who received an MHD diagnosis but no SUD diagnosis or indication of a pain management issue.
- Dual Diagnosis (DD): This agreement is for participants who received an SUD and MHD diagnosis but no indication of a pain management issue.
- Out-of-State: This agreement is for participants with a Michigan license who are working out-of-state and are monitored by an out-of-state program.
- Substance Use Disorder with Pain: This agreement is for participants who received an SUD diagnosis with a pain management issue related to the SUD diagnosis.
- Mental Health with Pain: This agreement is for participants who received an MHD diagnosis with a pain management issue related to the MHD diagnosis.
- Dual Diagnosis with Pain: This agreement is for participants who received an SUD and MHD diagnosis with a pain management issue related to the DD diagnosis (HPRP, 2021).

The most frequently occurring agreement type is for substance use disorder, as shown in Table 1.

Table 1 *Percentages of Participants by Program Agreement Type, 2019*

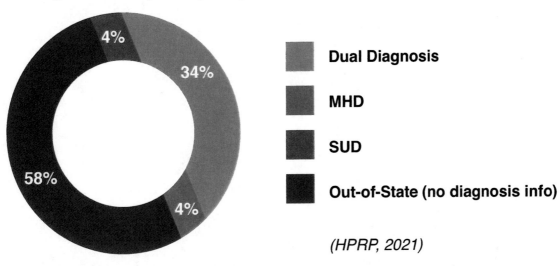

(HPRP, 2021)

Cases are monitored by experienced staff holding at least a master's degree in their professional field. Each week, all case managers attend a pre-team review and a clinical team review meeting to discuss changes to agreements, participant requests, compliance issues, and closure of cases.

HPRP Program Engagement and Length of Completion

Agreements initially require 1 to 3 years of monitoring, depending on the individual circumstances. Agreements can be extended to account for relapses and other instances of noncompliance with the agreed upon monitoring plan.

HPRP Completion Success Rates

90% or more of all participants remain compliant while in monitoring or are discharged after successfully completing the agreement each year. Only 10% or less are dismissed for failing to comply with program requirements each year.

If a participant has a noncompliant incident, they are not automatically dismissed from the program. Dismissal typically occurs as a last resort and only after the participant refuses to follow any new requirements that were put in place to address the noncompliant incident (HPRP, 2021).

Benefits of HPRP Participation

By supporting health professional licensees to enter treatment, the HPRP will serve to minimize the personal and societal losses which have occurred in the past when substance use and mental health disorders were treated as criminal acts. State of Michigan patients, residents and communities will benefit from the support for these professionals. The preservation of licensure with HPRP program participation retains both skill and experience to best preserve the ability of health professionals to continue to work in their professions and serve their communities in Michigan.

HPRP, HIPAA, and Participant Record Confidentiality

Until April 2015, all records regarding HPRP non-regulatory participants were destroyed after 5 years unless the participant became re-involved with the program during that 5-year time frame. Upon directive from legal counsel, all cases slated for destruction since April 2015 have been placed in a separate system making them unavailable to anyone but program administration and not destroyed. This directive was given to comply with document retention requirements during legal proceedings. These records will be destroyed upon the conclusion of these proceedings for individuals and are not attached to or discoverable with the individual's future license(s).

Telehealth, Telemedicine and Telecare

Telehealth, telemedicine and telecare are healthcare delivery entities that are becoming both more viable and utilized. The nurse should be aware of both the definitions and descriptions of telemedicine, and also the rules and legislation and implications for practice surrounding this health delivery mechanism.

Telecare

Telecare is the term that relates to ongoing technology that enables patients to maintain their independence and safety while remaining in their own homes. This technology includes mobile monitoring devices, medical alert systems, and telecommunications technology such as computers and telephones. Examples of this technology might include remote patient-monitoring tools such as blood pressure monitors, Bluetooth-enabled digital scales, blood sugar monitors, cardiac holter monitors and other wearable devices that can communicate biometric data to care providers for review. Continuous remote monitoring of patients enables telecare to track lifestyle changes over time and enables the provider to receive alerts relating to real-time emergencies.

Telemedicine

Telemedicine refers more specifically to education or intervention over a distance. Often, telemedicine refers to the provision of health care services through the use of varying telecommunications technology such as videoconferencing or audio-video communication tools. Telemedicine can be used to provide remote yet real-time clinical services to patients in their homes or at a location of their choosing. The digital transmission of medical imaging, remote medical diagnosis and evaluations, and video consultations with specialists are all examples of telemedicine (eVisit, 2020). Telemedicine can be synchronous (provider and patient interacting at the same time) such as a video call or phone consultation or asynchronous (provider and patient interacting at different times) such as through email, text messaging, stored video recordings or retrievable laboratory results or imaging. Both synchronous and asynchronous applications have viability for improved patient care delivery of services by increasing access regardless of time or appointment, such as for preliminary assessment of needed services or for immediate emergency behavioral health intervention (Guidelines, 2020).

Telehealth

Telehealth is a term that encompasses both telemedicine and telecare, and is used interchangeably with telemedicine (HHS, 2020).

Nurses' awareness of telemedicine as an option for patients to receive care or monitoring remotely may enhance treatment adherence and communication with providers and may assist in successfully meeting patient outcomes by removing barriers of travel, mobility, or general accessibility for patients.

The nurse should be aware of potential barriers with telehealth platforms that include access and navigation of technology, HIPAA confidentiality, Internet or phone connectivity issues, hearing or vision limitations, and varying insurance and Medicare/Medicaid reimbursement for services. An important part of the nurse's role in telehealth is to provide patient education regarding backup treatment options if the telehealth platform is not available or with technology failure.

Provider Autonomy in Telemedicine

Provider autonomy in telehealth has expanded due to the COVID-19 pandemic with increased provider reimbursement and scope of practice. Legislation surrounding provider ability to bill or be reimbursed for services that are remotely delivered is evolving, including considerations for waiving requirements that physicians and other health care professionals be licensed in the state in which they are providing services. Each state makes its own determination whether providers should have an equivalent licensing in the state of care delivery or in the licensing state of the provider.

Resources for telehealth can be found through the following organizations:

SAMHSA - Telebehavioral Health Training and Technical Assistance• American Telemedicine Association – Practical Guidelines for Video-based Online Mental Health

American Medical Association – Telemedicine: Connect to Specialists and Facilitate Better Access to Care for Your Patients

Getting Started with Telehealth: U.S. Department of Health and Human Services

American Psychological Association - Guidelines for the Practice of Telepsychology

Hazelden Betty Ford Foundation - Using Telehealth for Addiction Treatment

Workplace Violence

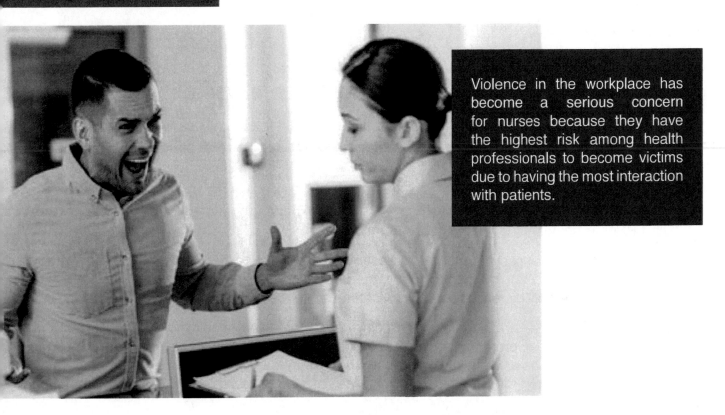

Violence in the workplace has become a serious concern for nurses because they have the highest risk among health professionals to become victims due to having the most interaction with patients.

Violence in the workplace has become a serious concern for nurses because they have the highest risk among health professionals to become victims due to having the most interaction with patients.

Definitions of workplace violence

Workplace violence is defined as the intentional use of physical force or emotional abuse, against an employee, that results in physical or emotional injury or consequences. This includes physical assault, threat, sexual harassment, and verbal abuse, which are defined as follows:

Physical assault - when you are hit, slapped, kicked, pushed, choked, grabbed, sexually assaulted, or otherwise subjected to physical contact intended to injure or harm you.

Threat - the use of words, gestures, or actions with the intent of intimidating, frightening, or harming (physically or otherwise).

Sexual harassment - any type of unwelcome sexual behavior (words or actions) that creates a hostile work environment.

Verbal abuse - when another person yells or swears at you, calls you names, or uses other words intended to control or hurt you. (MDHHS, 2020).

The Occupational Safety & Health Administration (OSHA, 2002) defines workplace violence as any physical assault, threatening behavior or verbal abuse occurring in the work setting.

Overall, verbal abuse is the most common type of violence experienced by nurses (85.9-100.0%), while sexual violence is the least common (24.4-62.6%; MDHHS, 2020).

Workplace Violence Victims

The professional groups at greatest risk for workplace violence are:

- Mental health technicians
- Nurses/nursing aides
- Security personnel

Incidence of workplace violence in Michigan nurses

In 2020, Michigan nurses were surveyed for the first time about their experiences with workplace violence. Slightly over one-third (35.6%) of RNs and one-quarter (25.1%) of LPNs reported experiencing workplace violence within the past year.

Younger RNs reported experiencing workplace violence at a higher rate than older RNs, while LPNs experienced workplace violence evenly across ages. Male nurses reported experiencing more workplace violence (42.4% RNs, 27.9% LPNs) as compared to female counterparts.

American Indian RNs experienced the most workplace violence (44.8%) while white LPNs experienced the most workplace violence (27.7%). The percent of nurses who reported experiencing workplace violence does not vary greatly geographically by residence or place of employment.

About half of the RNs (50.1%) who experienced workplace violence were employed as a nurse less than 3 years. Increased longevity in the profession equated with a lower rate at which the nurses reported experiencing workplace violence. There was an equal split between 3 to less than 10 years and 10 to less than 20 years (26.7% and 26.4% respectively) for LPNs reporting instances of workplace violence (MDHHS, 2020).

Perpetrators of workplace violence

The types of perpetrators or instigators of workplace violence that nurses may encounter include those individuals with no association with the workplace, a patient/customer of the workplace, a current/former employee, or someone with a personal relationship with employee(s) who is not currently in the workplace. All 4 types of workplace violence perpetrators occur in healthcare settings.

Patients and patient visitors are often perpetrators of *physical* violence, with likely violence ranging from scratching/biting to physical assault (Arnetz, et al, 2018).

Patients as perpetrators of workplace violence often have a current situation or background history of:

- Altered mental status
- Intoxication, substance abuse
- Delirium
- Psychosis
- Cognitive decline/dementia
- Angry, upset, worried
- Patients in pain
- Patients with history of violent behavior

In Michigan, patients are most commonly the perpetrators for both RNs (83.7-96.4%) and LPNs (83.3-94.9%) across all types of violence. Physical violence by patients is the most common type of patient-initiated violence perienced by RNs and LPNs (96.4% and 94.9% respectively). The family or friend of the patient is the next ost common perpetrator of violence for RNs (16.6-53.4%) and LPNs (8.0-38.2%) across all types of violence IDHHS, 2020).

ther employees or coworkers are often responsible for acts of non-physical violence, with violence ranging om verbal abuse to systematic bullying (Arnetz, et al, 2018).

ther employees or coworkers often display workplace violence through:

- Work behavior that is unprofessional such as disagreements or expressing dissatisfaction with co-worker, or
- Work organization, such as comments that a coworker failed to follow protocol, comments about patient assignments, or remarks about limited resources such as equipment or staff.

gain, verbal abuse is the most common type of violence experienced by nurses (85.9-100.0%; MDHHS, 2020).

Workplace Violence Settings

he most frequently occurring workplace violence settings in inpatient / acute care healthcare settings are:

- Psychiatric/mental health facilities
- Emergency departments
- Geriatric/dementia care units
- Pediatric units
- Intensive care units

he most frequently occurring workplace violence settings for out-of-hospital healthcare risk settings for orkplace violence are:

- Ambulance/EMS workers
- Nursing homes
- Outpatient mental health facilities
- Home health care (Arnetz, et al, 2018)

ithin healthcare settings, there are specific environmental factors that can exacerbate workplace violence, nd may include:

- Poor environmental design

    - Rooms/hallways or units with no means of escape from a violent event

    - Areas with blocked vision, such as curtained areas or rooms/doors without windows

    - Open access/lack of protective barriers for employees, such as waiting rooms or communal patient or visitor areas

- Lack of means of emergency communication
- Poor lighting (indoor and outdoor)
- Lack of metal detectors or screening of unwanted items into care areas (Arnetz, et al, 2018)

Michigan, nurses in behavioral health facilities (57.1%) and correctional systems (55.8%) experienced the ost workplace violence, while nurses in home health care had the lowest rate of experience with workplace olence (25.6%).

The community-based care setting was analyzed for RNs and LPNs together. In community settings, nurses in traveling or staffing agencies (45.9%) and correctional systems (44.3%) experienced the most workplace violence, while nurses at insurance companies had the lowest (13.2%) (MDHHS, 2020).

Consequences of Workplace Violence

Workplace violence can cause impacts to healthcare workers by changes in:

Individual health, such as physical injury, psychological effects such as fear, anger, depression/anxiety, post-traumatic stress disorder (PTSD) or burnout

Individual performance, such as decreased work satisfaction, less motivation, decreased ability to concentrate/focus or increased absenteeism

Overall organizational performance by aggregate increased sickness/ absence, higher turnover, increased organizational costs such as for replacement/recruitment, medical and legal expenses, etc.

Patient care outcomes are directly affected by workplace violence. Patients of nurses reporting bullying were significantly associated with the incidence of central line-associated bloodstream infections (CLABSI) on a unit level (Houck, 2017).

Workplace Violence Prevention

Preventing workplace violence consists of environmental interventions, organizational or administrative measures, and general behavioral and interpersonal strategies.

Environmental interventions can include design controls to discourage would-be assailants through control of entry/exits, lighting, alarm systems, physical separation of workers from customers and cashless, automated or virtual transactions.

Organizational and administrative measures to reduce workplace violence can include programs, policies and work practices aimed at maintaining a safe working environment such as zero tolerance policies, continuous assessment of risk situations, worksite walkthroughs, tracking & analyzing incident reports, enforcing policies, prohibiting violent behavior, and integration of strategies consistently into everyday working life of the unit/ hospital. There should be a culture of safety with no retaliation/reprisal for reporting abusive situations.

Behavioral and interpersonal strategies to reduce workplace violence include employee training programs on conflict resolution, self-defense techniques, post-incident support (de-briefing) and stress management. Healthcare employees should learn de-escalation techniques and timely reporting of all incidents they are involved in or observe (Arnetz, 2018).

In the 2020 Survey of Michigan Nurses, of those nurses who experienced workplace violence, a majority of RNs (86.8%) and LPNs (80.7%) reported having a process in place at their organization to report workplace violence incidents. However, there were some nurses who were unsure if there was a reporting process (10.2% RNs, 12.5% LPNs).

The majority of RNs and LPNs who experienced workplace violence in Michigan reported those incidents through their organizational-based reporting system (76.6% and 70.7% respectively). The next most common method of reporting a workplace violence incident was to the police or security (11.4% RNs, 7.6% LPNs). There were some RNs (10.4%) and LPNs (11.1%) who did not know the ways to report workplace violence (MDHHS, 2020).

Summary of Workplace Violence Prevention

...cts of workplace violence against nurses and healthcare workers can take various forms, including verbal and ...hysical abuse, bullying, harassment, exclusion, and intimidation, and can be targeted at and perpetrated by ...range of individuals. Perpetrators can include patients, visitors, colleagues, patients' family and friends, and ...anagement.

...orkplace violence can have far-reaching emotional, professional, physical, and psychological consequences. ...orkplace violence remains an issue for members of the nursing workforce. Addressing this issue will require ...collaborative effort that includes both recognition and documentation of incidents in hospital and community-...sed settings. Addressing the prevalence of workplace violence in health-care settings will have positive ...pacts for ethical, legal, and moral changes for the healthcare industry and will ultimately enhance the quality ...care provided and the longevity of our healthcare workers (Al-Qadi, 2021).

Index

References

ADA.gov (n.d.). Introduction to the ADA. http://www.ada.gov/ada_intro.htm.

Agency for Healthcare Research and Quality. (2018). *National healthcare quality and disparities report* (AHRQ Pub. No. 18-0033-EF). https://www.ahrq.gov/sites/default/files/wysiwyg/research/findings/nhqrdr/2017qdr.pdf

Agency for Healthcare Research and Quality. (2020). *National healthcare quality and disparities report* (AHRQ Pub. No. 20(21)-0045-EF). https://www.ahrq.gov/research/findings/nhqrdr/nhqdr19/index.html

Al-Qadi M. M. (2021). Workplace violence in nursing: A concept analysis. *Journal of occupational health*, 63(1), e12226. https://doi.org/10.1002/1348-9585.12226

American Association of Nurse Practitioners [AANP]. (2021). *Information and Resources for Michigan NPs*. https://www.aanp.org/advocacy/michigan

American Board of Professional Liability Attorneys [ABPLA](2021). *What is Malpractice?* http://www.abpla.org/what-is-malpractice.

American Nurses Association [ANA]. (2021). *Advanced Practice Registered Nurses (APRN)*. *https://www.nursingworld.org/practice-policy/aprn/*

American Nurses Association [ANA]. (2021). Nursing: Scope and Standards of Practice (4th Ed.). Silver Spring, MD. ANA.

Arnetz, J., Bengt,B., Arnetz,B. (2001). Violence towards health care staff and possible effects on the quality of patient care, *Social Science & Medicine*, 52(3),2001, 417-427. https://doi.org/10.1016/S0277-9536(00)00146-5.

Arnetz, J. E., Hamblin, L., Ager, J., Luborsky, M., Upfal, M. J., Russell, J., & Essenmacher, L. (2015). Underreporting of Workplace Violence: Comparison of Self-Report and Actual Documentation of Hospital Incidents. *Workplace health & safety*, 63(5), 200–210. https://doi.org/10.1177/2165079915574684

Arnetz, J, Hamblin, L, Sudan, S, Arnetz, B (2018). Organizational Determinants of Workplace Violence Against Hospital Workers, *Journal of Occupational and Environmental Medicine. 60*(8); 693-699.

Augenstein, J. (2020), *Opportunities to Expand Telehealth Use Amid the Coronavirus Pandemic.* https://www.healthaffairs.org/do/10.1377/hblog20200315.319008/full/

Bureau of Employment Relations: Wage and Hour Division (n.d.). Labor and Economic Opportunity. https://www.michigan.gov/leo/0,5863,7-336-94422_59886---,00.html

Campinha-Bacote, J. (2018). Cultural competemility: a paradigm shift in the cultural competence versus cultural humility debate – Part I. *The Online Journal of Issues in Nursing.* 2018; 24(1). Retrieved April 13, 2021 from https://ojin.nursingworld.org/MainMenuCategories/ANAMarketplace/ANAPeriodicals/OJIN/TableofContents/Vol-24-2019/No1-Jan-2019/Articles-Previous-Topics/Cultural-Competemility-A-Paradigm-Shift.html#Synergetic

Centers for Disease Control. (2021). Health equity: Racism and health. Retrieved April 12, 2021 from https://www.cdc.gov/healthequity/racism-disparities/index.html

Centers for Disease Control. (1993). *Healthy People 2000 Review, 1992.* National Center for Health Statistics, Public Health Service. https://www.cdc.gov/nchs/data/hp2000/hp2k92acc.pdf

Difference Between Telehealth and Telemedicine: Definition of Services. (2020, October 30). https://telehealth.hhs.gov/providers/getting-started/.

Difference Between Telehealth and Telemedicine: Definition of Services. eVisit. (2020, October 30). https://evisit.com/resources/what-is-the-difference-between-telemedicine-telecare-and-telehealth/.

Fitzgerald C, and Hurst S. (2017). Implicit bias in healthcare professionals: A systematic review. *BMC Med Ethics*; 18(1):19.

Guidelines for the Practice of Telepsychology. (2020, October 30). https://www.apa.org/practice/guidelines/telepsychology.

Health and Human Services (2020, November 2). *Your Rights Under HIPAA.* https://www.hhs.gov/hipaa/for-individuals/guidance-materials-for-consumers/index.html.

Health Professionals Recovery Program (2021). *Health Professionals Recovery Program: Serving Michigan Health Professionals Since 1994* [brochure]. 2016 HPRP Brochure (michigan.gov)

Houck, N, Colbert, A (2017). Patient Safety and Workplace Bullying. *Journal of Nursing Care Quality* 32(2)164-171.

Institute of Medicine. (2003). *Unequal treatment: Confronting racial and ethnic disparities in health care. Washington, D.C.*: National Academies Press. https://www.ncbi.nlm.nih.gov/books/NBK220362/

Joint Commission. (2016). *Implicit bias in health care*. https://www.jointcommission.org/assets/1/23/Quick_Safety_Issue_23_Apr_2016.pdf

Joint Commission for Accreditation of Healthcare Organizations [JCAHO](2019). *Workplace Violence Prevention Implementing Strategies for Safer Healthcare Organizations*. https://www.jointcommission.org/resources/patient-safety-topics/workplace-violence-prevention/workplace-violence-prevention-implementing-strategies-for-safer-healthcare-organizations/

Lai C.K., et al. (2014). Reducing implicit racial preferences: A comparative investigation of 17 interventions. *Journal of Experimental Psychology: General* 143(4):1765-85.

Licensing and Regulatory Affairs [LARA]. (n.d.). *Agency Contacts*. http://www.michigan.gov/lara/0,4601,7-154-76106-42245--,00.html.

Licensing and Regulatory Affairs [LARA]. (n.d.). *Director's Office – Board of Nursing; General Rules*. https://dtmb.state.mi.us/ORRDocs/AdminCode/1814_2018-033LR_AdminCode.pdf.

Licensing and Regulatory Affairs [LARA] (n.d.). *File a Complaint with BPL*. https://www.michigan.gov/lara/0,4601,7-154-89334_72600_73836---,00.html.

Licensing and Regulatory Affairs [LARA]. (n.d.). *Health Professional Licensing*. http://www.michigan.gov/lara/0,4601,7-154-89334_72600_72603---,00.html.

Licensing and Regulatory Agency [LARA]. (2021). *Health Professional Recovery Program*. LARA - Health Professional Recovery Program (michigan.gov)

Licensing and Regulatory Affairs: State of Michigan. (2021) *Licensing Information.*
https://www.michigan.gov/lara/0,4601,7-154-89334_72600_72603_27529_27542---
,00.html

Licensing and Regulatory Affairs [LARA]. (n.d.). *Nursing.*
http://www.michigan.gov/lara/0,4601,7-154-89334_72600_72603_27529_27542---
,00.html

Michigan Department of Health and Human Services [MDHHS](30 September, 2020). 2020
Survey of Michigan Nurses. *Office of Nursing Safety and Workforce Planning/ Michigan
Public Health Institute.*
https://www.michigan.gov/documents/mdhhs/MI_Nurse_Survey_Report_
2020_final_705633_7.pdf

Michigan Department of Health and Human Services [MDHHS] (2021). Behavioral Health and
Developmental Disabilities Administration.
https://www.michigan.gov/mdhhs/0,5885,7-339-71550_2941-146590--,00.html

Michigan Department of Health and Human Services. (2020). *Michigan COVID-19 task force on
racial disparities interim report.*
https://content.govdelivery.com/attachments/MIEOG/2020/12/03/file_attachments/16
16552/COVID-
19%20Task%20Force%20on%20Racial%20Disparities%20Interim%20Report.pdf

Michigan Department of Health and Human Services [MDHHS] (2016). *Your Rights When
Receiving Mental Health Services In Michigan.*
https://www.michigan.gov/documents/RightsBooklet_9716_7.pdf

Michigan Legislature (2021). *Michigan Mental Health Code.*
http://legislature.mi.gov/doc.aspx?mcl-258-1974-1

Michigan Department of Licensing Regulatory Affairs. (2021, June 1). *Department of licensing
and regulatory affairs bureau of professional licensing public health code – general
rules.* Retrieved 2021, June 15
from https://ars.apps.lara.state.mi.us/AdminCode/DownloadAdminCodeFile?FileName=
R+338.7001+to+R+338.7005.pdf&ReturnHTML=True.

Michigan Health Endowment Fund (2020). *Telehealth Information and Resources.*
https://mihealthfund.org/issues/telehealth

Michigan Legislature (2021). *Legislative Services Bureau : For the People, By the People: How State and Local Government Operate.*
https://www.legislature.mi.gov/Publications/StudentGuide.pdf

Michigan Legislature. (n.d.). *Michigan Legislature: Act 368 of 1978.*
http://www.legislature.mi.gov/(S(rvhy0ambvcigkkmfl35lhilk))/mileg.aspx?page=GetObject&objectname=mcl-act-368-of-1978.

Michigan Legislature (n.d.). *Michigan Legislature - Act 397 of 1978.*
http://www.legislature.mi.gov/(S(qmqlbl0sppldhxzgpzuhiigs))/mileg.aspx?page=GetObject&objectname=mcl-Act-397-of-1978.

Michigan Legislature. (n.d.). *Michigan Legislature: Section 333.17221.*
http://www.legislature.mi.gov/(S(yxp5hexn5c23vptdnyg5wawn))/mileg.aspx?page=getObject&objectName=mcl-333-17221.

Michigan Legislature. (n.d.). *Opinions.* http://www.michigan.gov/ag/0,4534,7-359-81903_2098800.html.

Michigan Legislature (2021). *Public Health Code: Act 368 of1978-Part 172; Nursing.*
https://www.legislature.mi.gov/documents/mcl/pdf/mcl-368-1978-15-172.pdf

Michigan Legislature. (n.d.). *Rulemaking Process Summary .*
https://www.michigan.gov/documents/lara/Rulemaking_Process_Summary_680004_7.pdf.

Montz, B. (2019, Aug 12). *Acronyms Explained.* Outright Action International. https://outrightinternational.org/content/acronyms-explained

Nagelkerk, J. M. (2006). *Starting your practice: a survival guide for nurse practitioners.* Mosby Elsevier. Pgs. 290-291

National Consortium of Telehealth Resource Centers (2020). *COVID-19 Telehealth Toolkit*. https://www.telehealthresourcecenter.org/wp-content/uploads/2020/03/Telehealth-and-COVID-19-FINAL.pdf

National Council of State Boards of Nursing [NCSBN]. (2021). *About NCBSN: History*. https://www.ncsbn.org/history.htm

National Council of the State Boards of Nursing [NCSBN]. (2021). *APRN Consensus Model: The Consensus Model for APRN Regulation, Licensure, Accreditation, Certification and Education*. https://www.ncsbn.org/aprn-consensus.htm

National Council of State Boards of Nursing [NCSBN]. (2021). *Computerized Adaptive Testing*. https://www.ncsbn.org/1216.htm

National Council of the State Boards of Nursing [NCSBN]. (2021). *History of APRN Advanced Practice Registered Nurses* (APRN). *https://www.ncsbn.org/737.htm*

National Council of State Boards of Nursing [NCSBN]. (2021). *How the NCLEX Works*. https://www.ncsbn.org/9009.htm

National Council of State Boards of Nursing [NCSBN]. (2020, July). *NCSBN Research Brief: 2019 NCLEX Examination Statistics* (Volume 79). https://www.ncsbn.org/2019_NCLEXExamStats.pdf

National Council for State Boards of Nursing [NCSBN]. (2021). *National Guidelines for Nursing Delegation. NCSBA and American Nurses Association [ANA]*. https://www.ncsbn.org/NGND-PosPaper_06.pdf

National Council of State Boards of Nursing [NCSBN]. (2021). *Next Generation NCLEX Project*. https://www.ncsbn.org/next-generation-nclex.htm

National Council of State Boards of Nursing [NCSBN]. (2020). *Summary of Modifications to the NCLEX-RN® and NCLEX-PN® Examinations Starting Oct. 1, 2020*. https://www.ncsbn.org/SummaryofModificationstoNCLEX.pdf

National Council of State Boards of Nursing. (2019, April). *Test Plan for the National Council Licensure Examination for Registered Nurses*. https://www.ncsbn.org/2019_RN_TestPlan-English.pdf

National Institutes on Minority Health and Health Disparities. (2021, February 11.) *In search of equity: Rethinking race and racism in science and medicine.* https://nimhd.blogs.govdelivery.com/2021/02/11/in-search-of-equity-rethinking-race-and-racism-in-science-and-medicine/

NCSBN. (2016) National Guidelines for Nursing Delegation. *Continuing Education Journal of Nursing Regulation.* www.ncsbn.org/NCSBN_Delegation_Guidelines.pdf

NCSBN. (1995). *Delegation decision-making process.* National Council of State Boards of Nursing 1995 Annual Meeting Business Book.

NCSBN. (1996). *Delegation: Concepts and decision-making process.* National Council of State Boards of Nursing 1996 Annual Meeting Business Book.

NLRB v. J. Weingarten, Inc., 420 U.S. 251 (1975). Justia Law. (n.d.). https://supreme.justia.com/cases/federal/us/420/251/.

Nursing Licensure (2021). *Advanced Practice Registered Nurse Requirements in Michigan.* https://www.nursinglicensure.org/np-state/michigan-nurse-practitioner/

Nursing Licensure (2021). *Nurse Practitioner Requirements: Change is in the Air.* https://www.nursinglicensure.org/articles/nurse-practitioner-license/

Polinski, J. M., Barker, T., Gagliano, N., Sussman, A., Brennan, T. A., & Shrank, W. H.(2016). Patients' satisfaction with and preference for telehealth visits. *Journal of General Internal Medicine [JGIM]*, 31(3), 269-275.

Richardson, J & Inghoglia, C. (2020). *Best Practices for Telehealth During COVID-19 Public Health Emergency* [pdf]. http://www.thenationalcouncil.org/wpcontent/uploads/sites/2/2020/03/National-Council-Telehealth-Best-Practices.pdf?daf=375ateTbd56

State of Michigan. (2020, April 6). Department of Licensing and Regulatory Affairs Director's *Office Board of Nursing – General Rules.* https://ars.apps.lara.state.mi.us/Transaction/DownloadFile?FileName=FinalRule.pdf&FileType=FinalRul

State of Michigan [SOM]. (n.d.). *State Departments. SOM - Departments.*
http://www.michigan.gov/som/0,4669,7-192-29701_29702_30045---,00.html.

Tatelbaum M. F. (2001). Needlestick safety and prevention act. *Pain physician, 4*(2), 193–195.

Unemployment Insurance Agency (n.d.). *Labor and Economic Opportunity*
https://www.michigan.gov/leo/0,5863,7-336-94422_97241---,00.html.

U.S. Department of Health and Human Services, Office of Minority Health. *National Partnership for Action to End Health Disparities. The National Plan for Action Draft as of February 17, 2010 [Internet]. Chapter 1; Introduction.*
http://www.minorityhealth.hhs.gov/npa/templates/browse.aspx?&lvl=2&lvlid=34

U.S. Department of Health and Human Services. *The Secretary's Advisory Committee on National Health Promotion and Disease Prevention Objectives for 2020. Phase I report: Recommendations for the framework and format of Healthy People 2020 [Internet]. Section IV: Advisory Committee findings and recommendations [cited 2010 January 6].*
http://www.healthypeople.gov/sites/default/files/PhaseI_0.pdf.

United States Department of Labor (n.d.) *About OSHA [Occupational Safety and Health Administration].* https://www.osha.gov/aboutosha.

U.S. Department of Labor (n.d.). *Continuation of Health Coverage (COBRA).*
https://www.dol.gov/general/topic/health-plans/cobra.

U.S. Department of Labor (n.d.). Family and Medical Leave Act.
https://www.dol.gov/agencies/whd/fmla.

U.S. Department of Labor (n.d.). Wages and the Fair Labor Standards Act.
https://www.dol.gov/agencies/whd/flsa

Workers' Disability Compensation Agency. (n.d.). *Workers' Disability Compensation Agency.*
https://www.michigan.gov/leo/0,5863,7-336-94422_95508---,00.html

World Health Organization. (2013, May 7). *Social determinants of health: key concepts.* https://www.who.int/news-room/q-a-detail/social-determinants-of-health-key-concepts

Notes

MI **NURSES**
Association

2310 Jolly Oak Road · Okemos, MI 48864
Ph. 517-349-5640 · 888.MI-NURSES · Fax 517-349-5818

www. minurses.org

facebook.com/minurses
twitter: @minurses